PREFACE

This magnificent Exhibition is in a literal sense unique, for never before has it been possible, even in their native country, for the arts of Portugal in all their variety to be assembled on so rich a scale. It may well be doubted whether such a project can ever be repeated.

The circumstances which have combined to make this Exhibition possible are themselves remarkable and, in the first instance, the Royal Academy must pay tribute to the owners and custodians of the works of art displayed here for their generosity in sparing their treasures, and for risking the hazards of what, in many instances, have been long and complicated journeys. Only one small object which the Executive Commission had wished to include was refused. Such a response, on a national scale, must be without parallel, and the owners of the relatively small number of works which were required from this country have been equally kind.

. The Royal Academy's indebtedness to the Government of Portugal cannot be sufficiently stressed. They have provided for the capital city of their oldest ally an Exhibition of Portuguese Art such as has never been presented; and by a gesture of quite exceptional munificence they have defrayed by far the larger part of the expenses. This far transcends the normal bounds of international friendship, and the Royal Academy recognises with grateful pride this privilege of revealing to the world a culture which has hitherto been largely inaccessible both to students and the art-loving public, and much of which is indeed barely accessible in its native country. Both for his part in negotiating these arrangements and for help in innumerable other ways, we are also immensely grateful to the Portuguese Ambassador, His Excellency Dr. Pedro Theotónio Pereira. He has given this Exhibition his enthusiastic support since the earliest stages of its planning.

Sir James Mann has pointed out in his Introduction that the planning, the selection and the arrangement of this Exhibition have been the work of one man, Professor Reynaldo dos Santos, with the expert assistance of the Secretary-General of the Executive Commission, Madame Irene Quilhó. In securing this display for London, this great authority on the arts of Portugal has never spared himself and it is no secret that he has at last realised one of his most cherished ambitions. But for Hitler's War, a Portuguese Exhibition, also to have been organised by Professor dos Santos, would have been held at

iii

the Royal Academy in the winter of 1940. The delay has not been in vain. His plans have become more ambitious and we have his own assurance that it would not have been possible fifteen years ago to have assembled so representative or so richly varied an Exhibition. Not only is Professor dos Santos world famous as a surgeon, but he has devoted years of his life to the study of the plastic arts. It is indeed due to his patriotism and his veneration for history that this Exhibition is so accurate and colourful.

I have been asked by the Professor to express, both on behalf of the Royal Academy and of the Executive Commission, their thanks to Sir James Mann, for his advice at all stages of the Exhibition and for his illuminating Introduction to this Catalogue; and to Mr. C. Vere Pilkington, for invaluable assistance especially in the translation and compilation of the Catalogue. Both of these authorities have wide knowledge of Portugal and her arts.

A. E. RICHARDSON

NOTE

The original documents of the Treaties on which the ancient Anglo-Portuguese Alliance is founded are now on view in the Museum of the Public Record Office, Chancery Lane, between the hours of 1 and 4 p.m. (Saturdays and Sundays excepted). They include documents of:

The earliest Treaty, dated 16 June, 1373.

The Treaty of Windsor, of 1386: "a perpetual league between the two countries."

Oliver Cromwell's Treaty of Peace and Commerce, 1654.

The Marriage Alliance of Charles II and Catherine of Braganza, 1661.

The Methuen Commercial Treaty of 27 December, 1703, under which the wine of Portugal was imported on more favourable terms than French wines.

PORTUGUESE ART
800 – 1800

Under Revision

WINTER EXHIBITION, 1955-56

ROYAL ACADEMY OF ARTS
LONDON

303271144P

ii

COMMITTEE

(Nominated by the Portuguese Government by Decree of
May 24, 1955)

PRESIDENT

PROFESSOR REYNALDO DOS SANTOS (President of the National
Academy of Fine Arts, Lisbon).

MEMBERS

DR. ANTÓNIO LUIS GOMES (Director-General of National Patrimony,
Ministry of Finance).

DR. ARMANDO DE CASTRO E ABREU (Chief of the Political Department
of the Ministry of Foreign Affairs).

DR. ANTÓNIO MEDEIROS GOUVEIA (Secretary of the Institute of Alta
Cultura).

DR. MÁRIO TAVARES CHICÓ (Professor of History of Art, Lisbon
University).

DR. JOÃO RODRIGUES DA SILVA COUTO (Director of the Museum de
Arte Antiga, Lisbon).

DR. JOSÉ DE BRITO CARREGAL DA SILVA PASSOS (Chefe do Gabinete,
Ministry of National Education).

DR. MANUEL ANTÓNIO DE OLIVEIRA MIRANDA (Chief of Finance
Department, Ministry of National Education).

EXECUTIVE COMMISSION

(Responsible for the selection, organisation and arrangement
of the Exhibition)

Director: PROFESSOR REYNALDO DOS SANTOS.

Secretary-General: MADAME IRENE QUILHÓ.

v

Map of
PORTUGAL
Indicating the places mentioned in the Catalogue

INTRODUCTION

By Sir James Mann

This winter it is the turn of Portugal to display her art in the Galleries of the Royal Academy.

With extraordinary generosity she has hazarded the treasures of churches, public buildings and museums to make this the most widely representative of all the great National Exhibitions that have been staged by the Royal Academy in recent years. The native genius of the other European countries, Flanders (twice), Holland (twice), Italy and France, was already familiar to the British public from extensive representation in our national collections. But the art of Portugal is very little known in this country, and Portuguese painting hardly at all. This time, too, the applied arts have been liberally brought in to round off the whole. Without them it would not be possible to understand the full range of Portuguese art and the great variety of sources from which it drew its inspiration.

Portugal is a small country like England, and occupies the westernmost strip of the great land-mass of the European Continent and Asia. Like England, her landscape varies greatly, ranging from the snows of the granite uplands of the Traz-os-Montes in the north to the semitropical vegetation of cork-trees and palms in the Alentejo in the south. She was the first of all the European countries to become a great maritime power, and the wealth that resulted from the early voyages of her captains to South America, Africa and the Far East has given her an historical importance out of all proportion to her size. The great period of Portuguese adventure and discovery was in the fifteenth century under the direction of Prince Henry the Navigator, whose mother was an English princess. In 1505 Portuguese ships sailed into Antwerp and offered Eastern wares at a cheaper rate than was to be had at Bruges, which until then had been the *entrepôt* for goods brought overland by caravans. This spelled the end of the golden age of Venice, which had hitherto held the monopoly of Eastern trade. In 1546 Portugal occupied the Spice Islands which are now part of Indonesia.

The interchange of ideas and forms between East and West can be seen here in countless details. There are the Portuguese soldiers carved in ivory from Benin in West Africa, the Portuguese ship depicted on a Japanese lacquer screen, the Holbeinesque portraits of

INTRODUCTION

Albuquerque and Dom João de Castro painted in Goa, the faience painted with Chinese decoration in Lisbon, not to mention the splendid Persian carpets which are casually introduced in many of the early religious paintings.

The visitor to Burlington House will from long habit look first at the pictures. In the second room he will be brought face to face with the nearly-life-size figures of the great Polyptych of St. Vincent by Nuno Gonçalves. The sculpturesque forms, the noble characterisation and the rich colour would mark him out as a great painter in any company. No work of his has ever before been shown in England. He ranks among the great masters of the fifteenth century outside Italy, and can be set beside the Maître de Moulins and Rogier van der Weyden. His hand is also to be seen in the design of the four panels of tapestry of the taking of Arzila by King Afonso. Though woven probably in Tournai, the cartoons are almost certainly by him, and details of arms, armour and costume belong exclusively to the Peninsula.

The Portuguese character is calm, friendly and unemotional. This is made apparent in so much of the work shown here. The religious paintings are devoid of gloom or emotional excess; even the saints and angels sculptured in wood and stone have pleasant round faces.

The influence of Flemish art is of course very strong, and some of these painters were of foreign birth, but it will be seen that the scale is often much larger than one is accustomed to with Flemish panels. The two large and airy compositions by Francisco Henriques, hung at the west end of Gallery III, are most arresting. The figures of the three saints, Cosmian, Damian and Thomas, are placed in space in a masterly manner that is entirely unexpected.

The Portuguese were great builders. The country provided excellent building stone, both limestone and granite. There arose the great Romanesque cathedrals of Lisbon, Coimbra and Oporto. A modern preference in ecclesiastical circles for the severe and grandiose conceptions of this style has led in recent times to the removal of the elaborately gilded baroque interior decoration with which they were "modernised" in the eighteenth century, and restoration has been more drastic than we like in this country. Of later date is the thirteenth-century monastery of Alcobaça, whose kitchen is so large that it has a natural river running through the middle of it. The great victory of Aljubarotta, in which a contingent of 500 English archers assisted, was commemorated, like the building of our own Battle Abbey, by another huge monastery in a curious version of the

Perpendicular style, reminding one more of Horace Walpole than John of Gaunt.

The most original contribution of Portugal to the history of architecture is the rich and ebullient Manueline style, named after the reigning King Manuel the Fortunate (1495–1521). Nothing could be more different from the contemporary Plateresque style in neighbouring Spain. The twisted pillars supporting the vaulting are strong and alive like trees, the deep carving of the decoration is exceptionally vigorous, taking plant and animal forms and incorporating them in fantastic patterns. The style can only be represented here by photographs and detached fragments, which give no idea of the way in which these exotic buildings of yellow and white stone, their detail thrown in high relief by a strong sun, stand out against a bright blue sky.

It is not for nothing that the shield of arms of Portugal has a border charged with castles. The country has no natural land frontier, and had to be surrounded with castles. The towers and battlements of these utilitarian structures also gave pleasure to the eye, and King Manuel had them recorded in a series of drawings by Duarte d'Armas, and the book is now in the National Archives at Lisbon. The Portuguese built castles at intervals along the west coast of Africa which are still in existence, and in Abyssinia that of Gondar survives as their memorial.

There is one branch of Portuguese art which has a special national character, but is sparsely represented here, namely, the tiles known as *azulejos*. They are used to cover buildings from floor to ceiling both inside and out, and give a brightness and gaiety to walls that would otherwise be plain and undistinguished. The early ones are purely mosarabic with geometrical patterns. Those who have visited the palace of Sintra near Lisbon will remember their intricate colours. In the seventeenth century these tiles are usually yellow, blue and green on white, and in the eighteenth century are limited to blue and white only and show pictorial scenes instead of arabesques. A group of them shown here record what Lisbon looked like before the disastrous earthquake of 1755, when so much of what was old and beautiful slid into the sea. It so happens that a few of these tiles have recently been placed on the garden wall of the new Portuguese Embassy in Belgrave Square to act as minor envoys of their country.

The goldsmith's work forms one of the most numerous sections of the Exhibition, and the lenders have been especially generous, as examples of native Portuguese mediaeval and Renaissance silver, both religious and secular, are very rare. A great many valuable eggs have been put

1*   ix

into one basket for our benefit. The earliest piece goes back to Visigothic times. The most splendid is the gold and enamelled monstrance of Belém, by Gil Vicente, the gift of King Manuel himself.

In 1580 Portugal passed under the dominion of Spain, but recovered her independence under the House of Braganza sixty years later. Some idea of the richness and profusion of the baroque and rococo periods are shown by the furniture and carved and gilt woodwork in the later rooms. It was intended to bring here the State Coach of King John V, one of the most thoroughgoing examples of rococo art in existence, but it was found to be too large, and an earlier and much soberer coach has come instead. The Museo de Coches is one of the sights of Lisbon, the series beginning with the sixteenth century and continuing until modern times. The splendid, heavy harness and saddlery and the liveries remain in excellent preservation.

The Exhibition ends with the early years of the nineteenth century, when many Englishmen became familiar with Portugal. Here can be seen Sequeira's portrait drawing of Lord Beresford, the English general, who was commandant of Lisbon in 1808 and was made a marshal in the Portuguese army and Conde de Trancoso.

In the past the Exhibitions at the Royal Academy have been the work of committees, but in the present case the choice of exhibits has been carried out by one man, Professor Reynaldo dos Santos. He is no stranger to this country, where he has been awarded the gold medals of the Royal Society and the Royal College of Surgeons. Somehow he has found time to travel widely and know the art of many countries besides his own, in which he stands supreme. To him and to his friend and pioneer, the late Dr. José de Figueredo, the discoverer of Nuno Gonçalves, is due the credit for this remarkable assemblage of works of art. Many of them have been brought from small churches in obscure villages, for dos Santos alone knows them all. Thanks to the Government of Portugal, they have now come for a few months to London, the capital of the country with which Portugal entered into a perpetual alliance by the Treaty of Windsor of 1386.

THE ART OF PORTUGAL, ITS CHARACTER AND DEVELOPMENT

By Professor Reynaldo dos Santos

In Portugal the mother art of architecture pursued a path roughly parallel to that of other countries of Western Europe; her most characteristic and idiomatic achievements were in the styles known as Romanesque, Manueline and Baroque. The photographs which have been arranged in a special section of the Exhibition will enable visitors to recognise the parallel development of the native styles of architecture and of the decorative arts.

In addition to those Romanesque cathedrals which were built under French influence, there are, scattered all over Portugal, more than a hundred Romanesque churches in a Portuguese idiom. Almost all are built of the local "granite" (a warm grey stone), of simple and harmonious proportions; the great blocks of stone of which they are made are meticulously cut and closely fitted. In scale, proportions and design these buildings blend perfectly into the countryside.

The Gothic style seems to have had little appeal to architects in Portugal, and the two outstanding examples, the great monasteries of Alcobaça and Batalha, show signs of French and of English design.

But in the reign of King Manuel (1495–1521), on the heels of the great Voyages of Discovery, an entirely individual Portuguese style made its appearance, which was neither Gothic nor Renaissance. In it the majestic simplicity of the Romanesque proportions was revived, overlaid by great exuberance of decoration mainly based on nautical *motifs*. Such was the Manueline style, a true expression of contemporary enthusiasm.

The refinements of the Renaissance reached Portugal mainly through the work of French artists who settled there: a true national style in architecture became once more apparent only in the Baroque period, at first in a more restrained seventeenth-century version, but later bursting with exuberance into decorative fantasy comparable with that of the Manueline period.

Sculpture

An essential unity of vision is the outstanding characteristic of Portuguese plastic art, and it is traceable through each period.

Except in Coimbra, the sculptured capitals from Romanesque

churches are mostly carved from the granite of the north. This material calls for simplicity of treatment, and so the carving is notable more for vigour than for delicacy.

In the fifteenth century, under the aura of the Gothic vision, Portuguese craftsmanship reached one of its pinnacles of achievement, which radiated over the country from the Coimbra School, and from that great master, Pero. The Gothic figures of the Virgin from Guimarães, Coimbra, Montemor and from Comandante de Vilhena's collection are examples of Pero's work: his masterpiece is the tomb of the Archbishop of Braga. Granite from the north, limestone from the Mondego Valley in the centre, marble from Estremoz and Vila Viçosa (e.g. the *St. Peter* from the Cathedral of Évora) were the local materials in which the sculpture of the fourteenth century was so splendidly realised. The tombs of King Pedro and the Lady Ines de Castro in the Abbey of Alcobaça are among the finest examples of European Gothic.

The figure-sculpture of the fifteenth century continued to reflect the spirit of the School of Coimbra. One of the masters whose work has been identified is João Afonso, to whom we owe the *St. Peter* from the Convent of Arouca, a work whose noble proportions enhance the dignified tranquillity of its conception. It is not surprising that Flemish and Burgundian influence was strong at the end of the fifteenth century, for Henry the Navigator's sister was married to the Duke of Burgundy, a wealthy patron of the Arts: it is in this period that a group of sculptors working at Coimbra, Tomar and Évora created a beautiful series of polychrome and gilt wood carvings.

The leading sculptors of the Renaissance period were French: Nicolau Chanterene, João de Ruão, Odarte and Francisco Loreto, to mention a few of the best-known names. They worked in Portugal for over thirty years and were profoundly influenced by the national style and environment. Nothing is so far known of their work outside their adopted country. At the end of this period the national tradition was once more re-asserted by the Master of St. Isabel. The style of the later seventeenth century Baroque was adopted by the sculptors employed on the redecoration of Alcobaça: working in terracotta on a massive scale, they created a more forceful style than their successors of the eighteenth century, who specialised in largely decorative carving for churches.

Although it has been found impossible to include in this Exhibition any of the great altar-pieces of the churches in Lisbon, Coimbra, Oporto or Évora, several smaller examples of the rich and splendid workmanship which graced the sculpture of this period are displayed.

There are also some photographs to show the magnificence of the altar-pieces of the King John V period (1720–*c.* 1750), of a more compact and balanced structure than their Spanish parallels.

PAINTING

The importance of Portuguese paintings of the fifteenth and sixteenth centuries may come as a surprise to the British public. The master who dominates the period is Nuno Gonçalves; by his breadth of vision, his charm and his skill in portraiture, his work will stand comparison with Van Eyck and his School, and with the great masters of the Italian *quattrocento*. His handling of the crowded composition of his masterpiece, the St. Vincent Polyptych, is a *tour de force*; it is like a tapestry in which the aerial and linear perspective are all subject to the importance of the narration; it is painted with the vision of a sculptor immersed in an introspective dream. Grouped round the figure of St. Vincent, the Patron Saint of the Nation and of the Royal House, we may see all classes of society, from the King to the pilgrim, from the Chapter of Lisbon and the Benedictine monks of Alcobaça to the Dukes of Braganza and the noble knights, sea-captains and generals, fishermen, Jews and Moors. . . . These are the "Lusiadas" of the fifteenth century of which the Portuguese poet Camoens sang a hundred years later.

The Portuguese school of the sixteenth century deserves a special niche in the history of European painting for its characterisation in portraiture, its large-scale composition and its vivid evocation of land- and seascape, its elegance of design and the beauty of the colour schemes, often dominated by the greys and the blacks which adumbrate the tonalities of Velasquez. In the present Exhibition there is a selection of works by the leading masters of this period—Francisco Henriques, Jorge Afonso, Frei Carlos, Cristovão de Figueiredo, Gregorio Lopes, Garcia Fernandes and the masters of the Viseu School, Vasco Fernandes and Gaspar Vaz. It may well be that the public will discover that the historians of European painting of this period have done less than justice to the Portuguese contribution.

In the seventeenth century the outstanding painter was Domingos Vieira, whose use of white highlighting owed something to the inspiration of El Greco. Portugal possesses in this same period a fine still-life painter, Josepha de Obidos.

There are few artists of mark in the eighteenth century, but at the turn of the century a great artist and designer of genius, Domingos António Sequeira, made his appearance. It is easy to see his affinities with his contemporary, Goya, but his special talents lie in a profound sense of chiaroscuro and a luminous vision foreshadowing Impressionism.

THE DECORATIVE ARTS

In certain periods, and particularly in the seventeenth century, the decorative arts in Portugal attained a high degree of originality and vigour. The craftsmen found their inspiration mainly in the architecture of the period, and in Oriental designs which were imported from the Far East, where Portuguese colonies and trading posts had been established since the late fifteenth century. But while from the end of the sixteenth century faience, furniture, Azulejos (glazed tiles), textiles and carpets were influenced by Chinese, Persian and Indian design, the goldsmith's art closely followed the main styles of contemporary Portuguese architecture.

The essential love of form is seen in the beautiful specimens of Romanesque goldsmiths' work, in which the decoration is enhanced by its restraint. The Coimbra Chalice and the Gold Cross of Dom Sancho are supreme examples of a refined sense of style. The gold and silver plate of the fifteenth and sixteenth centuries, which is shown in this Exhibition, forms a collection remarkable for any country: especially noteworthy are the typical salvers or tazzas and the ewers.

In the section devoted to the seventeenth century two tendencies are apparent: one towards plain silver of exquisite taste, the other towards more exuberantly Baroque decoration.

In the eighteenth century gold and diamonds from Brazil ushered in a period of immense wealth just as in the sixteenth century Portugal had been made rich by the Indian spice trade. But whereas King Manuel had entrusted native artists with the realisation of his ideas, King John V turned to Italian and French craftsmen to provide him with gold and silver plate, textiles, sculpture and even architecture, thereby strangling the national creative urge. If, in this period, execution displays the technical perfection of Portuguese goldsmiths' work, the design reflects an imported taste. Not until the close of the eighteenth century, in the neo-classical revival, did the craft of English goldsmiths, nearer akin to our own sober and classical taste, give to Portuguese art a new impulse and a new urge towards the revival of traditional forms. Domingos Sequeira was commissioned to design the gold and silver plate presented by the Portuguese nation to the great Duke of Wellington, and this is the last landmark of original inspiration before the general decadence of the goldsmith's art in Europe.

The Golden Age of the decorative arts, that is to say, of furniture,

xiv

pottery, Azulejos, textiles and carpets, was in the seventeenth century. This is strange because it was the century during which Portugal, until 1640, was subject to Spain and had been impoverished by nearly thirty years of the wars of Restoration which isolated her culturally from the rest of Europe: however, in spite of this it was a period of revival and of originality in the decorative arts. The Portuguese sailed to Brazil and the Far East, and it was from there that the new inspiration came. In particular the exciting imports of Oriental wares and the influence of Oriental design, which was later to attract the whole of Europe, inspired in simplified and assimilated form the Portuguese decoration of pottery, lacquer-work, textiles and embroidered carpets. It was Chinese porcelain which inspired the making and design of Portuguese faience of the seventeenth century, and it was the taste for Persian carpets which gave the impetus to the making of the Arraiolos crochet-work rugs. The hybrid Indo-Portuguese embroidery from Malacca, Cambaia and Goa set the Portuguese embroidering bedspreads at Castelo Branco, and it was the Chinese and Japanese lacquers which inspired the lovely Portuguese japanned work which is seen at its most exquisite best in the great Library of the University of Coimbra.

Her pioneer status in the Far East from the end of the fifteenth century made Portugal the earliest nation in Europe to comprehend and interpret Oriental design in national art.

As may be seen in the show-cases of faience, the Portuguese, under Chinese influence, were making glazed pottery earlier than Delft and at least from as early as the beginning of the seventeenth century. This is the less surprising when one realises that the Portuguese Governors of Malacca had been commissioning porcelain from China during the reign of King Manuel I.

The needlework carpets from Arraiolos were, until the eighteenth century, close to Persian design in their patterns and colouring, but after the turn of the century a more original and national character is apparent and their colouring becomes generally restricted to blues and yellows.

The vast imports of Indo-Portuguese furniture spread the taste for this all over the world; and the Exhibition includes a number of desks, tables and boxes made of Oriental woods, inlaid with ivory, bone and brass, in which one may catch reflections of the Mogul art of Delhi. This curious hybrid art is again apparent in the rich and original Indo-Portuguese bedspreads of the seventeenth century, where Portuguese figures, coats-of-arms, and ships are combined with Oriental decoration.

Oriental design and colour strongly influenced the art of the Azulejos, or tile-glazing, which developed in Portugal during the seventeenth century and which evolved into magnificently executed schemes of wall-decoration in polychrome, or in blue-and-white, on the interior and even exterior of churches, palaces, garden walls and pools.

The eighteenth century, the period when Portugal was so wealthy, was also the century in which a great number of works of art of all kinds were imported from England, France and Italy: this made for a decline in national originality of design, the contrary of the seventeenth century when a period of poverty had stimulated a revival of decorative craftsmanship and design, largely inspired by the assimilation of Oriental art. It must be said, however, that during the eighteenth century, both the decorative carving in wood and the art of the Azulejos reached a peak of originality and brilliance. Unfortunately it is not possible in such an Exhibition to represent adequately the applied decoration from churches and large country houses. However, as an example of the rich woodwork of the period, there are shown the carved doors from the celebrated Convent of Jesus at Aveiro. Some of the photographs will also help to give an idea of the imaginative power and the richly decorative effect of such works in their original setting.

GENERAL INFORMATION

THE Exhibition opens on Saturday, October 29, 1955, and closes on Sunday, February 19, 1956.

Hours of Admission: Week-days, 10 a.m. to 7 p.m.
Sundays, 2 p.m. to 6 p.m.

Price of Admission, 2s.   Season Ticket, 10s.

Catalogue, 1s. 6d. (by post 1s. 9d.).

Illustrated Souvenir, 3s. 6d. (by post 4s.).

SINGLE ADMISSION TICKETS

For the convenience of those who may wish to present them to their friends, Single Admission Tickets at 2s. each may be obtained at the Office of the Royal Academy.

REDUCED PRICE ADMISSIONS

Principals of recognised Schools of Art can obtain Season Tickets for Art Students on their registers at 5s. each.

Single admission tickets at a reduced price may be obtained for Schools and Members of Staff Associations, Guilds, and Working Men's and Girls' Clubs.   For particulars application should be made to the Secretary, Royal Academy of Arts, Piccadilly, W.1.

THE RESTAURANT,

(reached by the Staircase from the South Rooms)
is open for

LIGHT REFRESHMENTS:	from 11 a.m.
LUNCHEON:	12 noon to 2.30 p.m.
AFTERNOON TEA:	3 to 5.30 p.m.

(Sundays: 3 to 5 p.m.)

Visitors are required to give up their sticks and umbrellas before entering the Galleries; they must be left with the attendants at the Cloak Room in the Entrance Hall.   The other attendants are strictly forbidden to take charge of anything.

Invalids may obtain the use of a wheeled chair during certain hours, without charge, by previous arrangement with the Secretary, to whom application should be made for the necessary order.

xvii

PLAN AND CONTENTS OF THE GALLERIES

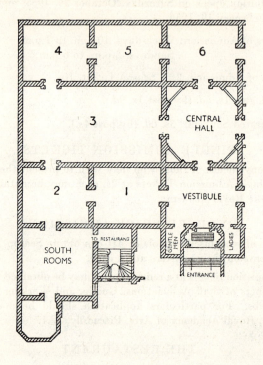

GALLERY 1.   IXth–XIVth Centuries

   „   2.   XVth Century

   „   3.   XVIth Century: Manueline

   „   4.   XVIth Century: Renaissance

   „   5.   XVIIth Century

   „   6.   XVIIIth Century

CENTRAL HALL.   XVIIth, XVIIIth and Early XIXth Centuries

LARGE SOUTH ROOM.   Portugal in the Orient, and Manuscripts

SMALL SOUTH ROOM.   Architectural Photographs

CATALOGUE

GALLERY I

1 Romanesque Capital carved with affronted Eagles and Mermen
Limestone. H. 40 cm. Early XIIth Century. From the Romanesque Church of St. Peter, Coimbra.
Lent by the Museu Machado de Castro, Coimbra.

2 Agnus Dei
Limestone. 75 × 90 cm. XIIth Century. From the Church of S. Miguel, Milreu.
Lent by the Museu Machado de Castro, Coimbra.

3 Romanesque Capital carved with Lions and Mermen
Limestone. H. 38 cm. Early XIIth Century. From the Romanesque Church of St. Peter, Coimbra.
Lent by the Museu Machado de Castro, Coimbra.

4 The Conquest of Arzila and Tangier: The Landing
Tapestry; wool and silk. 450 × 1050 cm. From the set of four modern replicas of originals woven in Flanders at the end of the XVth Century and now at Pastrana, Spain. The designs are attributed to Nuno Gonçalves. They represent the capture of Arzila and Tangier (Morocco) by King Afonso V of Portugal in 1471. No. 4 depicts the King and Prince John, dressed in the rich armour of the XVth Century, at first in a boat, later on land, surrounded by the Standards of Portugal, the Wheel of St. Catherine (Emblem of the King) and the Cross of St. George.
Lent by the Ministério das Finanças, Lisbon

MASTER PERO (Active 1330–1340)
5 The Virgin and Child (Fragment)
Limestone. H. 75 cm. From Montemor-o-Velho. Master Pero, the leading sculptor of the first half of the XIVth Century, worked mainly at Coimbra. The tombs of the Archbishop of Braga and of Queen Isabel are his most important works.
Lent by the Museu Machado de Castro, Coimbra.

19

In Case A (Nos. 6–18)

6 The Virgin and Child

Silver, parcel-gilt. H. 32·5 cm.   XVth Century.
Lent by the Museu de S. Roque, Lisbon.

7 Chalice

Silver-gilt, with traces of enamel. H. 17·3 cm.   On the cup, Christ and the Apostles; on the base, the symbols of the four Evangelists; filigree boss; inscribed: *GEDA MENENDIZ ME FECIT IN ONOREM SCI MICHAELIS E MCLXXXX* (A.D. 1152).   From the College of São Bento, Coimbra.
Lent by the Museu Machado de Castro, Coimbra.

8 Reliquary (Chasse)

Silver-gilt. H. 17 cm.   Inscribed in Gothic characters and dated *1419*.   Blazoned with the Arms of Dom Luiz Vasquez da Cunha.
Lent by the Museu de Guimarães.

9 Chalice

Silver-gilt. H. 17·1 cm.   Inscribed on the base: *CALIX ISTE AD HONOREM DEI ET SCĒ MARIE DE ALCOBACIA FACTUS EST.*   First half of the XIIth Century.   From the Monastery of Alcobaça.
Lent by the Museu de Arte Antiga, Lisbon.

10 Chalice

Silver-gilt. H. 16·3 cm.   Hemispherical, decorated with six embossed medallions, representing heraldic lions and foliage.   Inscribed on the base: *E: M: CC: XXV: REX SANCI: ET: REGINA: DVLCIA: OFFERUNT: CALICEM: ISTVM: STE: MARINE: DE: COSTA.*   Given by King Sancho I and Queen Dulce to the Monastery of Saint Marinha da Costa in 1187.
Lent by the Museu de Guimarães.

11 Chalice

Silver-gilt. H. 18 cm.   The boss in chased segments.   XIIth Century.   From the Monastery of Alcobaça.
Lent by the Museu de Arte Antiga, Lisbon.

12 Saint Nicolas

Silver, parcel-gilt. H. 59 cm.   Late XIVth Century.
Lent by the Museu Machado de Castro, Coimbra.

13   Holy Water Stoup and Sprinkler
Rock-crystal and silver-gilt.   H. 22·5 cm.   Decorated with stones and
Roman cameos.   Base with applied filigree work, XIIIth Century.
From the Monastery of Lorvão.
Lent by the Museu Machado de Castro, Coimbra.

14   Chalice
Silver-gilt.   H. 22 cm.   On the boss, jewels and filigree.   Inscribed
on the base: *IN: NÑE: DÑI: NR̃I: IH̃V: X: HUNC: CALICE:
DEDIT: REGINA: DULCIA: ALCUBACIE: IN: HONORE:
DEI: ET: GL̃OSE: VIRGINIS: MARIE: AD: ŠVIEVDV̄: IN:
MAJORE: ALTARE.*   XIIth Century.   From the Monastery of
Alcobaça.
Lent by the Museu de Arte Antiga, Lisbon.

15   Reliquary (Diptych)
Silver-gilt.   H. 24 cm.   Representing the Annunciation.   Romanesque
style.   Early XIIIth Century.
Lent by the Museu de Arouca.

16   Processional Cross
Rock-crystal and silver-gilt.   H. 61·5 cm.   Engraved in silver with
the Virgin and St. John and the emblems of the Evangelists.   The
boss and handle enamelled.   XIVth Century.
Lent by the Museu Machado de Castro, Coimbra.

17   Chalice and Paten
Silver-gilt.   H. 10·5 cm.   The Chalice decorated with vegetal-
motives, a lion and an eagle.   Inscribed: *MENENDUS GUNDI-
SALVI ET TUDA DOMNA SUM.*   The Paten decorated with
stylised foliage.   Mendo Gonçalves and his wife were the parents-in-
law of the King Afonso V of Leon.   Visigothic.   Late Xth Century.
Lent by the Sé de Braga.

18   Processional Cross
Rock-crystal and silver-gilt.   H. 57 cm.   In the centre an illuminated
miniature in Italianate style.   XIVth Century.
Lent by the Museu Machado de Castro, Coimbra.

SCHOOL OF MASTER PERO (Early XIVth Century)
19   The Virgin and Child
Stone, with traces of polychrome.   H. 90 cm.
Lent by the Museu Alberto Sampaio, Guimarães.

20 St. Peter
Marble, with traces of colour and gilding. H. 136 cm. Early XIVth
Century. From the Cloister of Évora Cathedral.
Lent by the Chapter of Évora Cathedral.

21 Armed Man on Horseback
Limestone. H. 72 cm. XIVth Century. From Oliveira do Hospital.
Lent by the Museu Machado de Castro, Coimbra.

MASTER PERO (Active 1330–1340)
22 St. Vincent (?)
Painted limestone. H. 127 cm.
Lent by the Museu Machado de Castro, Coimbra.

MASTER PERO (Active 1330–1340)
23 An Angel (from an *Annunciation*)
Painted limestone. H. 126 cm.
Lent by the Igreja da Senhora do Castelo, Montemor-o-Velho.

24 Capital representing the Descent of the Holy Ghost
Limestone, with traces of colour. H. 29 cm. Late XIIIth or early
XIVth Century. From the Convent of Celas, Coimbra.
Lent by the Museu Machado de Castro, Coimbra.

25 A Retable: The Corpus Christi
Polychrome stone. H. 112 cm.: W. 95 cm. With Gothic inscription
on the base and dated *1443*. Two kneeling Angels support the
Chalice. From the Chapel of the Church of Corpus Christi, Coimbra.
Lent by the Museu Machado de Castro, Coimbra.

26 The Conquest of Arzila and Tangier: The Siege
Tapestry; wool and silk. 450 × 1050 cm. From the set of four
modern replicas of originals woven in Flanders at the end of the XVth
Century and now at Pastrana, Spain. The designs are attributed to
Nuno Gonçalves. They represent the capture of Arzila and Tangier
(Morocco) by King Afonso V of Portugal in 1471. No. 26 depicts,
in the moat before the walls of the city, the King and Prince John on
horseback awaiting the moment of assault.
Lent by the Ministério das Finanças, Lisbon.

27 Processional Cross

Silver-gilt. H. 124 cm. Early XVth Century. From the Monastery of Alcobaça.

Lent by the Museu de Arte Antiga, Lisbon.

28 The Virgin and Child

Silver, parcel-gilt. H. 61·5 cm. Reliquary of the Holy Queen (Isabel), who died in 1336. With enamelled Arms of Aragon and Portugal. Early XIVth Century. From the Convent of Santa Clara.

Lent by the Museu Machado de Castro, Coimbra.

29 Processional Cross

Silver. H. 115 cm. A crucifix on one side and on the reverse the Agnus Dei and the symbols of the Evangelists. Made for a Knight Hospitaller, Afonso Mendes, in 1225. Romanesque style.

Lent by the Igreja de Poiares da Régua.

30 Visigothic Capital

Marble, with faint traces of polychrome. H. 42 cm. Xth Century. From Miranda do Corvo.

Lent by the Museu Machado de Castro, Coimbra.

31 Ninth Century Tombstone

Limestone. 66 × 202 cm. Christ in Majesty between two flying Angels and the four Evangelists. The Evangelists are represented with human bodies and symbolic heads of animals. From Dume, near Braga.

Lent by the Museu Diogo de Sousa, Braga.

In Case B

32 Processional Cross

Gold, pearls and precious stones. H. 61 cm. Inscribed: *DÑS SANCIUS REX JVSSIT FIERI HÃC † ANO ĨCARNATIONIS MCCXIIII.* Engraved on the back with the Agnus Dei and the emblems of the Apostles. Given by King Sancho I to the Monastery of Santa Cruz de Coimbra in 1214.

Lent by the Museu de Arte Antiga, Lisbon.

On the Screen (*Nos.* 33–34)

33 Christ on the Cross

Painted wood. H. 230 cm. Early XIVth Century. Formerly in the Oratorio das Donas, and later in the Monastery of Santa Cruz, Coimbra. This majestic work, by an unidentified artist, is certainly among the masterpieces of mediaeval art in Portugal.
Lent by the Museu Machado de Castro, Coimbra.

34 Romanesque Angel (Fragment)

Granite. H. 108 cm. Early XIIth Century. From Oporto Cathedral.
Lent by the Museu Machado de Castro, Coimbra.

GALLERY II

35 An Angel

Polychrome limestone. H. 77 cm. XIVth Century. From the Convent of Santa Clara, Coimbra.
Lent by the Museu Machado de Castro, Coimbra.

36 The Conquest of Arzila and Tangier: The Assault

Tapestry; wool and silk. 450 × 1050 cm. From the set of four modern replicas of originals woven in Flanders at the end of the XVth Century and now at Pastrana, Spain. The designs are attributed to Nuno Gonçalves. They represent the capture of Arzila and Tangier (Morocco) by King Afonso V of Portugal in 1471. No. 36 depicts the attack on the walls of Arzila. The King is represented on horseback, with the Royal Standard-bearer and the Standards of Portugal and St. George.
Lent by the Ministério das Finanças, Lisbon.

37 St. Anne with the Virgin and Child on her Knee

Stone. H. 65 cm. Late XVth Century.
Lent by Professor Reynaldo dos Santos, Lisbon.

PORTUGUESE SCHOOL (Late XVth Century)

38 Ecce Homo

Panel. 89 × 65 cm. Several replicas of this work exist. Exh: Paris, 1931.
Lent by the Museu de Arte Antiga, Lisbon.

NUNO GONÇALVES (Active 1450–1467)

39 St. Vincent Naked

Oak. 209 × 85 cm. From the Monastery of St. Vincent, Lisbon. Exh: Paris, 1931.
Lent by the Museu de Arte Antiga, Lisbon.

NUNO GONÇALVES (?) (Active 1450–1467)

40 St. Francis

Oak. 117 × 90 cm. This work and No. 45, which are certainly by the same hand, were probably parts of a great Reredos. From the Monastery of St. Vincent, Lisbon.
Lent by the Museu de Arte Antiga, Lisbon.

GALLERY II

MASTER OF AROUCA (Mid-XVth Century)

41 St. Peter

Stone, with traces of polychrome. H. 120 cm. From the Convent of Arouca. The Master of Arouca may perhaps be identified with João Afonso, the leading sculptor of the Coimbra school which flourished in the middle of the XVth Century. His masterpiece is the tomb of Fernão Gomes at Oliveira do Conde (1440).
Lent by the Museu de Arouca.

NUNO GONÇALVES (Active 1450–1467)

42 The Veneration of St. Vincent (Polyptych)

Tempera and oil on oak. Six panels, the two in the centre each 220 × 128 cm., the four flanking panels each 220 × 64 cm. Painted *c.* 1465–1467, for the Monastery of St. Vincent, Lisbon. First recognised and attributed to Nuno Gonçalves by José de Figueiredo in 1908. The panels portray the Court and the various groups of Portuguese Society in the great epoch of conquests and maritime discoveries. All these are shown in prayer before St. Vincent, the patron saint of Portugal and of the Royal House, possibly giving thanks for the capture of Alcacer in Morocco (1463). The principal figures in each panel, from left to right, are: (*a*) Three Benedictine monks of Alcobaça. (*b*) Three fishermen, with their net; the prostrate figure holding a rosary made of fish bones. (*c*) The Saint, with (in the right foreground) King Afonso V, behind whom stand Henry the Navigator and the young Prince John; the female figures on the left possibly represent (in the foreground) the deceased Queen Isabella and (behind) the widow of the first Duke of Braganza. The figure on the extreme left in the background is supposed to be a portrait of the artist. (*d*) The Saint, with (in the left foreground) the Constable Dom Ferdinand (brother of the King), surrounded by the main Captains of the Army and the Fleet; behind the Saint stand the Archbishop of Lisbon and his Chapter; on the extreme right, the King's Chronicler Azurera, and next to him the King's Physician. (*e*) The second Duke of Braganza and his sons, Dom Ferdinand and Dom John, with an unidentified Moorish nobleman, wearing a helmet of oriental design. (*f*) A monk presenting a relic of the Saint, a Jewish Rabbi and a Pilgrim.

By far the most important of the rare surviving works of this Master, who was mentioned by Francisco de Holanda in his *Dialogues* (1548) as ranking among the great European painters of his time, this polyptych is now becoming recognised as one of the masterpieces of European painting in the *quattrocento*. Exhibited in Paris in 1931

as two triptychs and now shown (for the first time outside Portugal) in its original arrangement.
Lent by the Museu de Arte Antiga, Lisbon.

FERNÃO MUNHOZ (Active 1510–1512)
43　St. Bernard

Polychrome and gilded wood. H. 142 cm. From the Monastery of Lorvão. The retable by Nuno Gonçalves formerly in the Cathedral at Lisbon, and destroyed in the earthquake of 1755, is known to have been designed around a central statue of St. Vincent and it is probable that the polyptych (No. 42) was similarly composed. This statue, and the canopy, which are both somewhat later, have been placed here to suggest the original composition.
Lent by the Chapter of Coimbra Cathedral.

44　St. Michael

Polychrome stone. H. 81 cm. XVth Century. From the Old Cathedral, Coimbra. Possibly by João Afonso or from his workshop.
Lent by the Museu Machado de Castro, Coimbra.

NUNO GONÇALVES (?)　(Active 1450–1467)
45　St. Teotonio

Oak. 115 × 88 cm. First attributed by Figueiredo to the workshop of Gonçalves, but approximating so closely in style to the hand of the Master that it is now widely regarded as authentic. From the Monastery of St. Vincent, Lisbon. Exh: Paris, 1931.
Lent by the Museu de Arte Antiga, Lisbon.

PORTUGUESE SCHOOL (Late XVth Century)
46　St. Ursula and St. Lawrence

Two panels from a triptych. Each 145 × 48 cm.
Lent by Professor Reynaldo dos Santos, Lisbon.

PORTUGUESE SCHOOL (Early XVth Century)
47　King John I

Panel. 41 × 32 cm. King John (1385–1415) married Philippa of Lancaster, daughter of John of Gaunt, and founded the great Aviz dynasty. He was the father of Henry the Navigator.
Lent by the Museu de Arte Antiga, Lisbon.

PORTUGUESE SCHOOL

48 Princess Joana

Panel. 62 × 42 cm. A copy of a lost original which may have been painted in the workshop of Nuno Gonçalves. Princess Joana (1451–1490) was a daughter of Afonso V. She entered a convent and was canonised.
Lent by the Museu de Aveiro.

49 The Conquest of Arzila and Tangier: The Occupation of Tangier

Tapestry; wool and silk. 450 × 1050 cm. From the set of four modern replicas of originals woven in Flanders at the end of the XVth Century and now at Pastrana, Spain. The designs are attributed to Nuno Gonçalves. They represent the capture of Arzila and Tangier (Morocco) by King Afonso V of Portugal in 1471. No. 49 depicts the surrender of the city to Dom John, son of the Duke of Braganza, after the capture of Arzila by the King. On the left, Portuguese horsemen are represented arriving at the gates of Tangier; on the right, the Moors surrender the city. In the centre, the bay and city of Tangier.
Lent by the Ministério das Finanças, Lisbon.

50 Gothic Chair

Oak, with modern restoration. H. 183 cm. Made in the second half of the XVth Century for the Monastery of Varatojo (Torres Vedras) and reputedly the chair used by King Afonso V during his year of retirement there.
Lent by the Museu de Arte Antiga, Lisbon.

51 An Angel

Polychrome limestone. H. 77 cm. XIVth Century. From the Convent of Santa Clara, Coimbra.
Lent by the Museu Machado Castro, Coimbra.

In Case C (Nos. 52–59)

52 Tazza

Silver-gilt. Diam. 32·5 cm. With diamond-point decoration. In the centre blazoned with the Arms of Costa, Castro Barreto and Brito. Marked with a Gothic *P* (Porto) and *LF*. Late XVth Century, the rim and stand of the XVIIIth Century.
Lent by the Fundação Ricardo Espirito Santo, Lisbon.

53 Tazza

Silver-gilt. Diam. 32 cm. Arbutus berry decoration and the Arms of the Soares family (of Toledo). Late XVth Century, the rim and stand of the XVIIIth Century.
Lent by the Misericórdia, Oporto.

54 Salver

Silver-gilt. Diam. 20 cm. Scenes of combat between primitive men and mythical beasts. The centre enamelled. Marked with a boat and two ravens (Lisbon) and *IM*. Late XVth Century.
Lent by the Victoria and Albert Museum, London.

55 Salver on Foot

Silver-gilt. Diam. 25 cm. Decorated with scenes of the Trojan War. (The iconography based on the Portuguese campaigns in Morocco.) Cf. the tapestries of Arzila (Nos. 4, 26, 36 and 49). Coll: Sir F. Cook; W. L. Hildburgh. Late XVth Century, the Arms of Pinto da Cunha added later.
Lent by the Victoria and Albert Museum, London.

56 Salver

Silver-gilt. Diam. 24 cm. Scenes of combat between primitive men and mythical beasts; in the centre, Saint George and the Dragon. Marked with a Gothic *P* (Oporto), *BN* and *V*. End of XVth Century.
Lent by the Palácio da Ajuda, Lisbon.

57 Salver

Silver-gilt. Diam. 23 cm. Arbutus berry decoration and enamelled centre. Late XVth Century.
Lent by Exmo. Sr. and S^ra. Burmester Martins, Oporto.

58 Salver

Silver, partly gilded. Diam. 26·4 cm. Decorated in diamond-point and with the arbutus berry and artichoke in the centre. Marked with a Gothic *P* (Porto) and *IZ*. Coll: W. L. Hildburgh. Late XVth Century.
Lent by the Victoria and Albert Museum, London.

59 Tazza

Silver-gilt. Diam. 34 cm. With diamond-point decoration and thistles. Marked with a Gothic *P* (Porto) and *AC* (or *AG*). Late XVth Century, the stand XVIIIth Century.
Lent by the Fundação Ricardo Espirito Santo, Lisbon.

In Case D (Nos. 60–67)

60 Salver on Foot

Silver-gilt. Diam. 26·5 cm. Scenes of combat between primitive men and mythical beasts. Late XVth Century, the rim and foot later.
Lent by the Palácio da Ajuda, Lisbon.

61 Dish

Silver-gilt. Diam. 25·2 cm. With two concentric bands decorated with lions, eagles, and other animals among leaves; the central flower encircled with thistles. Marked with a boat and two ravens (Lisbon) and *IM*. Second half of the XVth Century.
Lent by Exma. S^{ra.} Dona Amélia de Freitas G. Carvalho, Lisbon.

62 Tazza

Silver-gilt. Diam. 27 cm. With honey-comb decoration. Late XVth Century, the rim and foot of the early XVIIIth Century.
Lent by the Museu de Lamego.

63 Salver

Silver-gilt. Diam. 28·5 cm. Scenes of combat between primitive men and mythical beasts, an artichoke in the centre. Late XVth Century, the rim later.
Lent by the Museu de Arte Antiga, Lisbon.

64 Salver on Foot

Silver-gilt. Diam. 27·5 cm. Scenes of combat between primitive men and mythical beasts, an enamelled flower in the centre. XVth Century.
Lent by the Museu de Arte Antiga, Lisbon.

65 Tazza

Silver-gilt. Diam. 27 cm. With honey-comb decoration. Late XVth Century, the rim and foot of the early XVIIIth Century.
Lent by the Museu de Lamego.

66 Dish

Silver-gilt. Diam. 28·5 cm. Decorated with lions, bears, horses, griffins, etc.; in the central medallion a thistle encircled by leaves. Marked with a boat (?), and a Gothic P (Porto) and $\tilde{A}R$. Style of the XVth Century.

Lent by Comandante Ernesto de Vilhena, Lisbon.

67 Salver

Silver-gilt. Diam. 23·4 cm. Scenes of combat between primitive men and mythical beasts. Marked with a boat and two ravens (Lisbon) and *IM*. XVth Century.

Lent by Exmo. S^{r.} and S^{ra.} Engenheiro Pedro Inácio Alvares Ribeiro, Oporto.

GALLERY III

FERNÃO MUNHOZ (Active 1510–1512)

69   An Angel with the Arms of Portugal

Polychrome wood.   H. 158 cm.   From the Monastery of the Order of Christ, Tomar.

Lent by the Monastery of the Order of Christ, Tomar.

CRISTOVÃO DE FIGUEIREDO (Active 1515–1540)

70   The Martyrdom of St. Hipolito

Panel.   117 × 101 cm.   From the University of Coimbra.   Figueiredo studied under Jorge Afonso (see No. 84).   One of the strongest personalities and perhaps the best colourist of the Portuguese School of the XVIth Century, he was the favourite painter of Queen Leonor.

Lent by the Museu de Arte Antiga, Lisbon.

Attributed to CRISTOVÃO DE FIGUEIREDO (Active 1515–1540)

71   Ecce Homo

Panel.   185 × 141 cm.

Lent by the Igreja de Santa Cruz, Coimbra.

FRANCISCO HENRIQUES (Active 1500–1518)

72   Saints Cosmian, Thomas and Damian

Panel.   254 × 206 cm.   Painted 1509–1511.   From the Monastery of São Francisco, Évora.   Henriques settled in Portugal from Flanders in 1500.   The Flemish character of his art was influenced, notably in the expansion of his compositions to a more monumental scale, by his years in Portugal.

Lent by the Museu de Arte Antiga, Lisbon.

CRISTOVÃO DE FIGUEIREDO (Active 1515–1540)

73   Triptych

Three poly-centric panels, each 259 × 128 cm., in their original frame, with canopy and crowned Arms.   The panels represent: (*a*) The Way of the Cross. (*b*) Calvary. (*c*) The Burial of Our Lord.   Commissioned for the Church of Caldas da Rainha by Queen Leonor, *c.*

1524. The shape of the frame, in characteristic Manueline style, conforms with the poly-centric form of the supporting arch, for which it was designed.
Lent by the Igreja de Nossa Senhora do Populo, Caldas da Rainha.

74 Monstrance

Silver-gilt. H. 80 cm. Decorated in enamel with figures of Angels. Inscribed and dated: *ESTA CUSTODIA FOI ACABADA NA ERA DE 1534.*
Lent by the Museu de Guimarães.

75 Pair of Candlesticks

Rock-crystal with a gilt base, bands and candle-guard. H. 40 cm. XVIth Century.
Lent by the Museu Machado de Castro, Coimbra.

DIOGO PIRES THE ELDER (Active 1471–1485)

76 The Virgin and Child

Polychrome limestone. H. 110 cm. A beautiful and characteristically delicate work by the last important Portuguese sculptor of the Gothic period. His relationship to Diogo Pires the Younger, who worked in the Manueline style, is unknown.
Lent by Comandante Ernesto de Vilhena, Lisbon.

77 Bishop's Crozier

Silver-gilt. H. 235 cm. On the boss, in niches, the figures of St. Paul, St. Peter and the four Evangelists. On the crook, the emblems of the Passion in niches. The image of the Annunciation in the scroll. Set with semi-precious stones and blazoned with the Arms of Athaydes e Aguiares. XVIIth Century. From the Monastery of São Bento da Avé Maria do Porto.
Lent by the Museu de Arte Antiga, Lisbon.

78 Altar Frontal

Green velvet; the borders embroidered in red and gold. 120 × 244 cm. XVIth Century. From the Convent of Graça, Lisbon.
Lent by the Museu de Arte Antiga, Lisbon.

2   33

FRANCISCO HENRIQUES (Active 1500–1518)

79 Our Lord appearing to St. Mary Magdalen

Panel. 246 × 198 cm. Painted 1509–1511. From the Monastery of São Francisco, Évora.

Lent by the Museu de Arte Antiga, Lisbon.

CRISTOVÃO DE FIGUEIREDO (Active 1515–1540)

80 The Entombment, with portraits of two Donors

Panel. 182 × 155 cm. The portraits of the Donors are remarkable as foreshadowing the work of Velasquez, whose father was Portuguese. From the University of Coimbra. Exh: Paris, 1931.

Lent by the Museu de Arte Antiga, Lisbon.

CRISTOVÃO DE FIGUEIREDO (Active 1515–1540)

81 The Martyrdom of St. Andrew

Panel. 118 × 101 cm. From the University of Coimbra.

Lent by the Museu de Arte Antiga, Lisbon.

FERNÃO MUNHOZ (Active 1510–1512)

82 St. Michael

Polychrome wood. H. 158 cm. From the Monastery of the Order of Christ, Tomar.

Lent by the Monastery of the Order of Christ, Tomar.

83 Manueline Capital with Royal Emblems

Stone. H. 33 cm. Early XVIth Century.

Lent by the União dos Amigos dos Monumentos da Ordem de Cristo, Tomar.

PORTUGUESE SCHOOL (Early XVIth Century)

84 The Resurrection

Panel. 410 × 252 cm. Reynaldo dos Santos has suggested that this may be one of the hitherto unidentified works of the master Jorge Afonso, in whose workshop Cristovão Figueiredo, Garcia Fernandes, Gregorio Lopes and Gaspar Vaz are all known to have studied.

Lent by the Monastery of the Order of Christ, Tomar.

OLIVÉRIO DE GAND (Active 1498–1512) AND FERNÃO MUNHOZ (Active 1510–1512)

85 The Virgin and St. John

Polychrome wood. H. 146 cm. From the Monastery of the Order of Christ, Tomar. Early XVIth Century.

Lent by the Monastery of the Order of Christ, Tomar.

86 The Triumph of Dom John de Castro

Tapestry; wool and silk with gold and silver thread. 345 × 530 cm. From the set of ten woven in Brussels c. 1555 to commemorate the triumph of Dom John de Castro at Goa after the capture of Diu in 1547. No. 86 depicts Dom John de Castro leaving the castle to attack the city walls.

Lent by the Kunsthistorisches Museum, Vienna.

THOMÉ THE ELDER (Active 1556–1582)

87 St. Elisabeth

Stone. H. 157 cm. From the Old Cathedral, Coimbra. Thomé the Elder was a pupil of João Afonso. He led the revival of a severely national style in sculpture in reaction against the fashionable French influence.

Lent by the Museu Machado de Castro, Coimbra.

Attributed to CRISTOVÃO DE FIGUEIREDO (Active 1515–1540)

88 Calvary

Panel. 255 × 155 cm.

Lent by the Misericórdia de Setubal.

MASTER OF SANTIAGO (Early XVIth Century)

89 Four Scenes from a Polyptych

Four panels, each 127 × 84 cm. The scenes represent: (a) St. James preaching. (b) St. James and Hermogenes. (c) Investiture of a Knight of the Order of Santiago (St. James). (d) Vision of a Master of the Order of Santiago. Painted by a follower of Cristovão de Figueiredo. Exh: Paris, 1931.

Lent by the Museu de Arte Antiga, Lisbon.

Attributed to CRISTOVÃO DE FIGUEIREDO (Active 1515–1540)

90 Christ Nailed to The Cross

Panel. 196 × 110 cm.

Lent by the Misericórdia de Setubal.

MASTER OF SÃO BENTO (Active *c.* 1520)

91 The Adoration of the Magi

Panel. 176 × 133 cm. The artist may be Cristovão de Figueiredo, working with Garcia Fernandes. Originally in the Monastery of São Francisco da Cidade, Lisbon, afterwards in the Monastery of São Bento. Exh: Bordeaux, 1954.
Lent by the Museu de Arte Antiga, Lisbon.

PORTUGUESE SCHOOL (Mid-XVIth Century)

92 Inferno

Panel. 119 × 217 cm.
Lent by the Museu de Arte Antiga, Lisbon.

93 Bas-relief of Manueline Arms and Emblems

Polychrome wood. Diam. 200 cm. Part of a Manueline roof, probably from the Royal Palace at Coimbra. The Cross of Christ, the Arms of King Manuel and Queen Maria and Armillary Spheres. Early XVIth Century.
Lent by the Museu Machado de Castro, Coimbra.

GREGORIO LOPES (*c.* 1500–1550)

94 The Virgin and Child with Angels in a Garden

Panel. 127 × 167 cm. Painted *c.* 1536. From the Monastery of the Order of Christ, Tomar. Exh: Bordeaux, 1954. Gregorio Lopes studied under Jorge Afonso, the leading painter at the beginning of the XVIth Century (none of whose works can now be definitely identified), whose daughter he married. Lopes succeeded Afonso as chief painter to the Court.
Lent by the Museu de Arte Antiga, Lisbon.

MASTER OF THE MADRE DE DEUS RETABLE (Early XVIth Century)

95 The Nativity

Panel. 167 × 139 cm. Painted for the Convent of Madre de Deus, Lisbon. Attributed by José de Figueiredo to Cristovão Lopes, the son of Gregorio Lopes.
Lent by the Museu de Arte Antiga, Lisbon.

MASTER OF SÃO BENTO (Active *c.* 1520)
96 The Visitation
Panel. 181 × 133 cm. From the same Reredos as No. 91 and probably the work of the same two artists in collaboration. From the Monastery of São Francisco da Cidade, Lisbon.
Lent by the Museu de Arte Antiga, Lisbon.

PORTUGUESE SCHOOL (Early XVIth Century)
97 St. John the Baptist Preaching
Panel. 140 × 107 cm. Probably by a follower of Gregorio Lopes. From the same Retable as No. 107.
Lent by the Museu de Arte Antiga, Lisbon.

MASTER OF THE PARADISE (Active *c.* 1530–1540)
98 Four Panels from an Altar-piece
Four panels, each 128 × 87 cm. From the Monastery of Paraíso, Lisbon. The scenes represent: (*a*) The Annunciation. (*b*) The Nativity. (*c*) The Visitation. (*d*) The Flight into Egypt. Probably from the studio of Gregorio Lopes and certainly painted under his influence.
Lent by the Museu de Arte Antiga, Lisbon.

UNKNOWN ARTIST (Early XVIth Century)
99 Shipping Scene
Panel. 76 × 144 cm. Depicting the Portuguese Fleet, bearing the Flags and Emblems of King Manuel, meeting Italian ships (on the right), possibly on the occasion of the Infanta Dona Beatriz's journey to marry the Grand Duke of Parma. Painted *c.* 1520.
Lent by the National Maritime Museum, Greenwich.

SCHOOL OF THE MASTER OF SARDOAL (Early XVIth Century)
100 Saint Vincent
Panel. 123 × 70 cm. Exh: Bordeaux, 1954.
Lent by the Museu de Béja.

GARCIA FERNANDES (Active 1514–1565)
101 St. Vincent
Panel. 126 × 55 cm.
Lent by the Igreja de Santa Cruz, Coimbra.

102   **The Triumph of Dom John de Castro**

Tapestry; wool and silk with gold and silver thread.   345 × 530 cm.
With an inaccurate inscription and date (1538)   From the set of ten
woven in Brussels *c.* 1555, to commemorate the triumph of Dom John
de Castro at Goa after the capture of Diu in 1547.   No. 102 depicts
Dom John de Castro returning to Goa after the conquest of the five
Capitals of Hidalção.
Lent by the Kunsthistorisches Museum, Vienna.

DIOGO PIRES THE YOUNGER (Active 1491–1530)

103   **Guardian Angel, with the Arms of Portugal**

Stone.   H. 175 cm.   From the Monastery of Santa Cruz, Coimbra.
Lent by the Museu Machado de Castro, Coimbra.

GREGORIO LOPES (Active 1514–1550)

104   **The Beheading of St. John the Baptist**

Panel.   239 × 120 cm.   In the background, a view of the Templars'
Church, Tomar.   From the same Retable as Nos. 105–106, painted for
the Church of St. John, Tomar, *c.* 1530–1540.
Lent by the Igreja de São João Baptista, Tomar.

GREGORIO LOPES (Active 1514–1550)

105   **Gathering the Manna**

Panel.   174 × 123 cm.
Lent by the Igreja de São João Baptista, Tomar.

GREGORIO LOPES (Active 1514–1550)

106   **The Presentation of the Head of St. John the Baptist**

Panel.   242 × 123 cm.
Lent by the Igreja de São João Baptista, Tomar.

PORTUGUESE SCHOOL (Early XVIth Century)

107   **St. Jerome**

Panel.   140 × 99 cm.   Probably by a follower of Gregorio Lopes.
From the same Retable as No. 97.
Lent by the Museu de Arte Antiga, Lisbon.

GALLERY III

On the Screens (Nos. 108–112)

MASTER OF SANTA AUTA (*c.* 1520)

108 *Recto*: **St. Ursula and Prince Conan.** *Verso*: **The Relics of St. Auta Leave Cologne**
Panel. 68 × 73 cm. See No. 110. Commissioned by Queen Leonor for the Church of Madre de Deus, Lisbon. Exh: Paris, 1931.
Lent by the Museu de Arte Antiga, Lisbon.

MASTER OF SANTA AUTA (*c.* 1520)

109 **The Martyrdom of the Eleven Thousand Virgins**
Panel. 93 × 192 cm. The artist can almost certainly be identified as Cristovão de Figueiredo. Commissioned by Queen Leonor for the Church of Madre de Deus, Lisbon. Exh: Paris, 1931.
Lent by the Museu de Arte Antiga, Lisbon.

MASTER OF SANTA AUTA (*c.* 1520)

110 *Recto*: **Pope Cyriacus blesses St. Auta and Prince Conan.** *Verso*: **The Relics of St. Auta arrive at the Church of Madre de Deus, Lisbon.**
Panel. 75 × 76 cm. See No. 108. Commissioned by Queen Leonor for the Church of Madre de Deus, Lisbon. Exh: Paris, 1931.
Lent by the Museu de Arte Antiga, Lisbon.

MASTER OF SARDOAL (Active early XVIth Century)

111 **St. Catherine and St. Barbara**
Panel. 56 × 71 cm.
Lent by Exmo. S^r. Vasco Bensaude, Lisbon.

MASTER OF SARDOAL (Active early XVIth Century)

112 **Two Bishops with the Shield of Queen Leonor and her Emblem**
Panel. 56 × 71 cm.
Lent by the Museu de Évora.

In Case E (Nos. 113–124)

113 **Salver**
Silver with traces of gilt. Diam. 28 cm. Decorated with a frieze of artichokes within horse-shoe compartments. The central medallion embossed with a floral emblem. Marked with a Gothic *P* (Porto) and *AG*. Late XVth Century.
Lent by Exmo. S^r. José Van Zeller Palha, Vila Franca de Xira.

114 **Dish**

Silver-gilt. Diam. 57·5 cm. Biblical scenes in three concentric circles and Portuguese inscription; in the centre, a circle of thistles. Manueline style, first quarter of the XVIth Century. The initials in silver *MF*, added in mid-XIXth Century.
Lent by the Palácio da Ajuda, Lisbon.

115 **Ewer**

Silver-gilt. H. 47 cm. Decorated with thistles and artichoke leaves on the lid; the handle and spout with mythical figures. Manueline style, early XVIth Century.
Lent by the Palácio da Ajuda, Lisbon.

116 **Salver on Foot**

Silver, parcel-gilt. Diam. 27 cm. In the centre, Arms of the Ribeiro family. Marked with a boat (Lisbon) and *AR*. First half of the XVIth Century.
Lent by the Fundação Ricardo Espirito Santo, Lisbon.

117 **Box**

Silver-gilt. Diam. 8·5 cm. With the Arms of Bishop D. Jorge d'Almeida. (1483–1543).
Lent by the Museu Machado de Castro, Coimbra.

118 **Dish**

Silver-gilt. Diam. 53 cm. Scenes and allegories from Portuguese history, with the Manueline emblem of the Cross on the ships. Manueline style, first quarter of the XVIth Century.
Lent by the Palácio da Ajuda, Lisbon.

119 **Salver**

Silver, with traces of gilding. Diam. 25 cm. Decorated with two bands of curved and radiating drapery. Early XVIth Century, the central medallion of later date.
Lent by Professor Reynaldo dos Santos, Lisbon.

120 **Salver on Foot**

Silver-gilt. Diam. 32 cm. With African scenes and the Royal Arms in the centre. First half of the XVIth Century.
Lent by the Palácio da Ajuda, Lisbon.

121 Salver on Foot

Silver-gilt. Diam. 27 cm. Embossed with circular studs in a network of cables; the Paschal Lamb in the centre encircled with mythical figures and foliage. Late XVth Century.
Lent by the Palácio da Ajuda, Lisbon.

122 Hour-Glass

Silver-gilt. H. 18·5 cm. With the Arms of King Manuel and the armillary sphere at either end. Manueline style, *c.* 1520.
Lent by the Museu de Arte Antiga, Lisbon.

123 Salver on Foot

Silver-gilt. Diam. 32 cm. With African scenes and the Royal Arms in the centre. First half of the XVIth Century.
Lent by the Palácio da Ajuda, Lisbon.

124 Salver on Foot

Silver-gilt. Diam. 23·5 cm. Decorated with primitive men and the Arms of the Mellos or Castros family. Early XVth Century.
Lent by the Fundação Ricardo Espirito Santo, Lisbon.

In Case F (Nos. 125–134)

125 Dish

Silver-gilt. Diam. 54 cm. Decorated with scenes of battle in Africa, a Knight holding a standard with the Arms of Coutinhos (hereditary Marshals). Manueline style, first quarter of the XVIth Century.
Lent by the Palácio da Ajuda, Lisbon.

126 Armorial Dish

Silver-gilt. Diam. 47 cm. Decorated with dragons, angels and centaurs. Manueline style, first quarter of the XVIth Century.
Lent by the Museu Machado de Castro, Coimbra.

127 Ewer

Silver-gilt. H. 47 cm. Decorated in Renaissance style. Second quarter of the XVIth Century.
Lent by the Museu Machado de Castro, Coimbra.

128 Dish

Silver-gilt. Diam. 57·5 cm. With scenes on three concentric bands: the Seven Deadly Sins, Samson and Delilah, the Judgment of Solomon, Joseph in Egypt, the Seven Virtues. Manueline style, first quarter of the XVIth Century.
Lent by the Palácio da Ajuda, Lisbon.

129 Tazza
Silver-gilt. Diam. 34·5 cm. Representing an attack on a fortified town; on a standard, the Arms of Portugal. Manueline style, the border and stand added at the beginning of the XVIIIth Century, with the Arms of the Sás family.
Lent by the Palácio da Ajuda, Lisbon.

130 Chalice
Silver-gilt. H. 26 cm. Hexagonal base and stem, embossed with thistles. Manueline style, beginning of XVIth Century.
Lent by the Museu de Arte Antiga, Lisbon.

131 Reliquary in the form of a bust of a Saint
Silver-gilt. H. 32 cm. Made to enshrine the relics of five Franciscans martyred in Morocco. Dated *1510*.
Lent by the Igreja de Santa Cruz, Coimbra.

132 Reliquary Cross
Silver-gilt. H. 45 cm. In flamboyant Gothic style. Late XVth Century.
Lent by the Museu de Arouca.

133 Chalice
Silver-gilt. H. 31·1 cm. Chased with figures of the Virgin and Child, Angels and Saints. Manueline style. Early XVIth Century.
Lent by the Museu Machado de Castro, Coimbra.

134 Salver
Silver-gilt. Diam. 37 cm. Battle scenes with a fortified town and boats. Manueline style, first quarter of the XVIth Century. The rim and stand added at the beginning of the XVIIIth Century, with the Sás Arms. The stand with the mark of Lisbon and *AM*.
Lent by the Palácio da Ajuda, Lisbon.

---

135 Manueline Fountain
Stone. H. 108 cm. Carved with the Arms of King Manuel I and Queen Leonor. Early XVIth Century.
Lent by the Museu de Arte Antiga, Lisbon.

136 Bishop's Cope

Red velvet with gold brocading; the hood and borders embroidered in gold and silk. H. 118 cm. XVIth Century. From the Monastery of the Jerónimos, Belém.
Lent by the Museu de Arte Antiga, Lisbon.

137 Bishop's Cope

Green velvet; the hood and borders embroidered in red and gold. H. 119 cm. XVIth Century. From the Convent of Graça, Lisbon.
Lent by the Museu de Arte Antiga, Lisbon.

138 The Belém Monstrance

Gold and enamel. H. 73 cm. The Gothic base divided into compartments decorated with birds, snails, sea-shells, etc., and inscribed: *O. MVITO. ALTO. PRICIPE. E. PODEROSO. SENHOR. REI. DO. MANVEL. I. A. MDOV. FAZER. DO. OVRO. I. DAS. PARIAS. DE. QILVA. AQVABOV. E. CCCCCVI.* (1506). The boss formed as armillary spheres. The kneeling figures of the Apostles in polychrome enamel. Surmounted by a canopy of exquisite gold tracery in Gothic–Manueline style, enshrining the figure of the Eternal Father and the Dove. This famous Monstrance, one of the most precious Portuguese possessions, was commissioned by King Manuel I from the goldsmith Gil Vicente.
Lent by the Museu de Arte Antiga, Lisbon.

139 A Prophet

Stone. H. 50 cm. Early XVth Century. From the Monastery of Batalha.
Lent by the Museu de Arte Antiga, Lisbon.

GALLERY IV

PORTUGUESE SCHOOL (Late XVIth Century)

140 Portrait of a Nun

Panel. 75 × 54 cm. The painter of this fine portrait has not been identified but was possibly a follower of Cristovão de Figueiredo. Exh: Paris, 1931.

Lent by the Museu de Arte Antiga, Lisbon.

GASPAR VAZ (Active 1514–1568)

141 Saint Michael

Panel. 215 × 173 cm. Painted between 1531 and 1540 for the Monastery of S. João de Tarouca. Gaspar Vaz, a pupil of Jorge Afonso, worked mainly in Viseu.

Lent by the Bishop of Lamego.

ODARTE (Active 1530–1540)

142 An Apostle (from a *Last Supper*)

Terracotta. H. 160 cm. Completed in 1534 for the refectory of the Monastery of Santa Cruz, Coimbra. In 1866 it was transferred, already damaged, to the Museum. Odarte, of French origin, worked for a time in Spain and is known to have settled in Portugal by 1530. He was perhaps the strongest artistic personality among the group of French sculptors working there at that epoch.

Lent by the Museu Machado de Castro, Coimbra.

FREI CARLOS (Active 1517–1540)

143 The Virgin and Child

Panel. 30 × 22 cm. Painted for the Monastery of the Jerónimos, Lisbon. Frei Carlos, an artist of Flemish birth and training, entered the Monastery of Espinheiro, Évora, in 1517. All his known works were painted there.

Lent by the Museu de Arte Antiga, Lisbon.

PORTUGUESE SCHOOL (Early XVIth Century)

144 Vasco da Gama

Panel. 25 × 20 cm. The identification of the sitter is traditional. Exh: Paris, 1931.

Lent by the Museu de Arte Antiga, Lisbon.

MASTER OF VISEU (Early XVIth Century)

145 Four Scenes from a Polyptych

Four panels, each 134 × 82 cm. The panels represent: (a) The
Nativity. (b) The Adoration of the Magi. (c) Our Lord in the Garden.
(d) The Descent from the Cross. Painted for the Cathedral of Viseu,
c. 1505. According to XVIIth Century chroniclers the artist was
Vasco Fernandes. Later authorities have noted affinities with the
earlier style of Francisco Henriques. The painter was more probably
an unidentified artist working under the influence of one of these
masters.
Lent by the Museu de Grão Vasco, Viseu.

VASCO FERNANDES (c. 1480–1543)

146 Calvary

Panel. 242 × 240 cm. With three *predelle*: (a) Christ before Pilate.
(b) The Deposition. (c) The Descent into Hell. Vasco Fernandes,
also known as Grão Vasco, was born at Viseu and worked mainly in
this region. He and Cristovão Figueiredo are the dominating artistic
personalities in Portuguese painting of their period.
Lent by the Museu de Grão Vasco, Viseu.

147 Chest

Carved wood. H. 52 cm.: W. 62 cm.: L. 100 cm. Early XVIth
Century.
Lent by the Museu de Arte Antiga, Lisbon.

GREGORIO LOPES (Active 1514–1550)

148 St. Anthony

Panel. 34 × 29 cm. From the Convent of Jesus, Setubal.
Lent by the Museu de Arte Antiga, Lisbon.

ODARTE (Active 1530–1540)

149 An Apostle (from a *Last Supper*)

Terracotta. H. 160 cm. From the same *Last Supper* as No. 142.
Lent by the Museu Machado de Castro, Coimbra.

VASCO FERNANDES (c. 1480–1543)

150 The Descent of the Holy Spirit

Panel. 161 × 163 cm. Signed *Velascs*. Painted 1535. In the
original Renaissance frame.
Lent by the Church of Santa Cruz, Coimbra.

NICOLAU CHANTERENE (Active 1515–1550)

151 The Virgin (from an *Annunciation*)

Stone. H. 98 cm. Executed *c.* 1520. Originally in the Ameal Collection, Coimbra. Chanterene, the main sculptor of the Renaissance period in Portugal, was of French origin. His greatest work is the tomb of King Manuel I and Queen Maria in the Jerónimos, Lisbon.

Lent by the Museu Machado de Castro, Coimbra.

VASCO FERNANDES (*c.* 1480–1543)

152 St. Peter

Panel. 216 × 233 cm. In three *predelle*: a Hermit, St. Jerome and St. Anthony. From the Sacristy of Viseu Cathedral.

Lent by the Museu de Viseu.

VASCO FERNANDES (*c.* 1480–1543)

153 The Creation of the Animals

Panel. 170 × 85 cm. From an Altar-piece painted for the Cathedra of Lamego, 1506–1511. Exh: São Paulo, 1954.

Lent by the Museu de Lamego.   •

NICOLAU CHANTERENE (Active 1515–1550)

154 Column, Capital and Entablature

Pink Estremoz marble. Dated *1533*. Formerly in the Convent of Paraíso, Évora. Later transferred to the Lisbon Museum, and then to the Museu d'Évora.

Lent by the Museu d'Évora.

PORTUGUESE SCHOOL (Mid-XVIth Century)

155 The Last Judgment

Panel. 214 × 176 cm. From the Monastery of São Bento, Lisbon. Probably by a follower of Garcia Fernandes. A panel from the same altar-piece is signed *VA* and dated *1549*.

Lent by the Museu de Arte Antiga, Lisbon.

MASTER OF LOURINHÃ (Active early XVIth Century)

156 St. John on Patmos

Panel. 150 × 137 cm. The composition is derived from a number of Flemish prototypes and the artist may have been a follower of Francisco Henriques. Exh: Bordeaux, 1954.

Lent by the Hospital da Misericórdia, Lourinhã.

GALLERY IV

CRISTOVÃO DE MORAIS (Active late XVIth Century)
157 **King Sebastian**
Canvas. 99 × 85 cm. Exh: Paris, 1931.
Lent by the Museu de Arte Antiga, Lisbon.

PORTUGUESE SCHOOL (Early XVIth Century)
158 **Prince John with his Patron**
Panel. 158 × 68 cm. Painted *c.* 1515, probably by a follower of
Francisco Henriques. Prince John succeeded his father King
Manuel in 1521.
Lent by the Museu de Arte Antiga, Lisbon.

MASTER OF ABRANTES (Active mid-XVIth Century)
159 **Four Scenes from an Altar-piece**
Four panels, each 121 × 87 cm. (*a*) The Annunciation. (*b*) The
Nativity. (*c*) The Way of the Cross. (*d*) Calvary. Painted for the
Misericórdia de Abrantes in about 1550.
Lent by the Misericórdia de Abrantes.

NICOLAU CHANTERENE (Active 1515–1550)
160 **An Angel with the Shield of St. Clare**
Polychrome stone. H. 85 cm. From the Convent of Santa Clara,
Coimbra.
Lent by the Museu Machado de Castro, Coimbra.

MASTER OF SANTOS-O-NOVO (*c.* 1540)
161 **Four Scenes from an Altar-piece**
Four panels, each 134 × 120 cm. The scenes represent: (*a*) The
Annunciation. (*b*) The Adoration of the Shepherds. (*c*) Jesus
in the Garden. (*d*) The Resurrection. From the workshop of
Gregorio Lopes and painted for the Monastery of Santos-o-Novo,
Lisbon.
Lent by the Museu de Arte Antiga, Lisbon.

FREI CARLOS (Active 1517–1540)
162 **St. Francis receiving the Stigmata**
Panel. 177 × 77 cm.
Lent by the Museu de Arte Antiga, Lisbon.

FREI CARLOS (Active 1517–1540)
163 Our Lord Appearing to His Mother
Panel. 151 × 119 cm. Dated *1529*. From the Monastery of Espinheiro, Évora.
Lent by the Museu de Arte Antiga, Lisbon.

FREI CARLOS (Active 1517–1540)
164 The Good Shepherd
Panel. 100 × 65 cm. Exh: Paris, 1931.
Lent by the Museu de Arte Antiga, Lisbon.

JOÃO DE RUÃO (JOHN OF ROUEN, Active 1530–1580)
165 An Angel (from an *Annunciation*)
Polychrome stone. H. 80 cm. Executed *c.* 1538. From the Convent of Santa Clara, Coimbra. João de Ruão, French by birth, is known to have spent most of his life at Coimbra. He married a sister of Cristovão Figueiredo. One of the most influential sculptors of the Renaissance period in Portugal, his naturalistic style is somewhat commonplace and lacking in strong personality.
Lent by the Museu Machado de Castro, Coimbra.

FREI CARLOS (Active 1517–1540)
166 The Ascension
Panel. 154 × 120 cm. Exh: Paris, 1931; Bordeaux 1954.
Lent by the Museu de Arte Antiga, Lisbon.

FREI CARLOS (Active 1517–1540)
167 St. Anthony and the Holy Child
Panel. 173 × 74 cm.
Lent by the Museu de Arte Antiga, Lisbon.

168 Arraiolos Carpet
Wool embroidery. 213 × 340 cm. Persian design in green and red. Early XVIIth Century. From the Monastery of Calvário, Évora.
Lent by the Museu de Arte Antiga, Lisbon.

In Case G (Nos. 169–178)
169 Tazza
Silver-gilt. Diam. 34 cm. The Triumphs of Cæsar; inscribed in a shield: *Iulio Sezar*. Renaissance style, second quarter of the XVIth Century. The border and stand added early in the XVIIth Century, with the Arms of the Sás family. The stand marked *L* (Lisbon) and *AM*.
Lent by the Palácio da Ajuda, Lisbon.

170 **Crown**
Silver-gilt. H. 13·5 cm. Set with semi-precious stones. Late
XVIth Century.
Lent by the Museu Machado de Castro, Coimbra.

171 **Tazza**
Silver-gilt. Diam. 37 cm. Decorated with scenes of battle in
Renaissance style. Early XVIth Century, the rim and stand
added at the beginning of the XVIIIth Century. The stand marked
L (Lisbon) and *AM*.
Lent by the Palácio da Ajuda, Lisbon.

172 **Ewer**
Silver-gilt. H. 43 cm. Decorated with bas-relief figures in Renais-
sance style. Second quarter of the XVIth Century.
Lent by the Palácio da Ajuda, Lisbon.

173 **Crown**
Silver-gilt. H. 15 cm. Set with clusters of semi-precious stones.
End of the XVIth Century.
Lent by the Museu Machado de Castro, Coimbra.

174 **Tazza**
Silver-gilt. Diam. 35·5 cm. The Triumphs of Alexander. Renais-
sance style, second quarter of the XVIth Century. The rim and stand
added early in the XVIIIth Century, with the Arms of the Sás family.
The stand marked *L* (Lisbon) and *AM*.
Lent by the Palácio da Ajuda, Lisbon.

175 **Tazza**
Silver-gilt. Diam. 35 cm. Decorated with scenes of combat in
Renaissance style. XVIth Century. Rim and stand added in the
XVIIth Century, with the Arms of the Duque de Bragança.
Lent by the Palácio da Ajuda, Lisbon.

176 **Tazza**
Silver-gilt. Diam. 31 cm. Decorated with grotesque figures and
Renaissance themes. Second quarter of the XVIth Century.
Rim and stand added early in the XVIIIth Century, with Episcopal
Arms (Dom Gaspar de Bragança).
Lent by the Palácio da Ajuda, Lisbon.

49

177 Salver on Foot

Silver-gilt. Diam. 31 cm. With Biblical scenes and the Arms of Souza Prados. Renaissance style. Second quarter of the XVIth Century.
Lent by the Palácio da Ajuda, Lisbon.

178 Tazza

Silver-gilt. Diam. 30 cm. Decoration in Renaissance style. XVIth Century. The rim and stand and Episcopal Arms added in the XVIIIth Century.
Lent by the Palácio da Ajuda, Lisbon.

In Case H (Nos. 179–188)

179 Salver

Silver-gilt. Diam. 32 cm. Fluted decoration and the Arms of Vasco da Gama's descendants. Late XVIth or early XVIIth Century.
Lent by the Museu de S. Roque, Lisbon.

180 Censer

Silver-gilt. H. 24 cm. Spherical form. Given to the Cathedral of Coimbra by Dom Afonso de Castelo Branco (1585–1615).
Lent by the Museu Machado de Castro, Coimbra.

181 Ewer

Silver, parcel-gilt. H. 34 cm. Renaissance decoration, with the Arms of Souza Prados on the lid. XVIth Century.
Lent by the Palácio da Ajuda, Lisbon.

182 Dish

Silver, parcel-gilt. Diam. 51 cm. Decorated with grotesque figures in Renaissance style and the Arms of Souza Prados. Second quarter of the XVIth Century.
Lent by the Palácio da Ajuda, Lisbon.

183 Pyx

Silver-gilt. H. 17·3 cm. Engraved in Renaissance style and surmounted by the Virgin in gold and enamel. On the inside of the lid, an enamel medallion with an eagle. Marked with a Gothic *P* (Porto) and a leaf. Mid-XVIth Century.
Lent by Exmo. S^r. Francisco de Barros e Sá, Lisbon.

184 Ewer and Dish
Silver, parcel-gilt. (Ewer) H. 29 cm.; (Dish) Diam. 29 cm. Simple Renaissance form with the Royal Arms. Made by the goldsmith Luiz Gonçalves, *c.* 1551.
Lent by the Capela da Universidade, Coimbra.

185 Censer
Silver, lightly gilded. Diam. 21·5 cm. Spherical form with the Arms of Bishop Mendes de Távora (1638–1646).
Lent by the Museu Machado de Castro, Coimbra.

186 Tazza
Silver-gilt. Diam. 34·5 cm. Renaissance decoration. Early XVIth Century. The rim and stand, with the Arms of the Sás family, added early in the XVIIIth Century.
Lent by the Palácio da Ajuda, Lisbon.

187 Chalice
Silver-gilt. H. 37 cm. Renaissance decoration, set with semi-precious stones. Attributed to Simão Ferreira. End of the XVIth Century.

188 Tazza
Silver-gilt. Diam. 35 cm. Decorated with scenes from the life of Christ in Renaissance style. Early XVIth Century. The rim and stand, with the Arms of the Sás family, added early in the XVIIIth Century.
Lent by the Palácio da Ajuda, Lisbon.

In the Doorway

189 Sanctuary Lamp
Silver. H. 136·5 cm. Made by the goldsmith Simão Ferreira, of Coimbra. Dated *1597*.
Lent by the Capela de Universidade, Coimbra.

GALLERY V

191 Baroque Angel

Polychrome terracotta. H. 80 cm. Early XVIIth Century. Probably from the Monastery of Alcobaça.
Lent by the Museu de Arte Antiga, Lisbon.

PORTUGUESE SCHOOL (Mid-XVIIth century)

192 Catherine of Braganza

Canvas. 124 × 103 cm.
Lent by the Museu d'Évora.

193 Pair of Chairs

Chestnut; carved stretchers, the seats and backs covered with red velvet; brass studs and finials. H. 102 cm. XVIIth Century.
Lent by the Museu d'Évora.

194 Cabinet on Stand

Tortoiseshell, lavishly mounted with brass fittings and studs.
H. 111 cm. Indo-Portuguese style, XVIIth Century.
Lent by Exma. S^{ra.} Dona Amélia de Freitas G. Carvalho, Lisbon.

195 Dish

Silver. Diam. 41 cm. Plain silver with radiating fluting. Marked L (Lisbon) and *AA*. Early XVIIIth Century in the style of the XVIIth.
Lent by the Museu de S. Roque, Lisbon.

196 Arraiolos Carpet

Wool embroidery. 186 × 124 cm. Geometrical decoration. In blue, green and yellow. XVIIth Century.
Lent by the Fundação Ricardo Espirito Santo, Lisbon.

197 Arraiolos Carpet

Wool embroidery. 192 × 123 cm. Polychrome decoration. XVIIth Century.
Lent by the Fundação Ricardo Espirito Santo, Lisbon.

198 **Panel of Tiles (Azulejos)**
In polychrome. 88 × 90 cm. XVIIth Century.
Lent by the Museu d'Évora.

199 **Tabernacle:**
Carved and gilded wood. H. 162 cm. Renaissance style. Early
XVII Century.
Lent by the Museu de Aveiro.

200 **Lobed Bottle**
Faience. H. 42 cm. With hunting and fishing scenes in blue and
white. Lisbon, XVIIth Century.
Lent by Exmo. Sr. Antonio Russel de Sousa, Oporto.

201 **Chair**
Walnut and embossed leather; brass studs and finials. H. 137 cm.
Inscribed: *Pereira.* First half of the XVIIth Century.
Lent by the Museu de Arte Antiga, Lisbon.

DOMINGOS VIEIRA (Active 1627–1652)
202 **Dona Isabel de Moura**
Canvas. 38 × 29 cm. Exh: Paris, 1931.
Lent by the Museu de Arte Antiga, Lisbon.

203 **Bedspread**
Carmine silk on green silk. 307 × 220 cm. Indo-Portuguese decora-
tion. Early XVIIIth Century.
Lent by the Fundação Ricardo Espirito Santo, Lisbon.

In Case I (Nos. 204–233)

204 **Two-handled Wine Cup**
Silver. Diam. 9·5 cm. With lobed decoration. XVIIth Century.
Lent by Dr. Augusto Lamas, Lisbon.

205 **Salver on Foot**
Silver. Diam. 24 cm. With fluted decoration and on the base
inscribed: *Barbara do Spirito Santo.* Late XVIIth Century.
Lent by the Museu Machado de Castro, Coimbra.

206 **Ewer**
Silver. H. 34·6 cm. With a high crooked handle. Marked *P* (Porto) and with a flower of four petals. Made at the end of the XVIIth Century in the style of late XVIth.
Lent by the Fundação Ricardo Espirito Santo, Lisbon.

207 **Inkstand and Bell**
Silver. L. 20·5 cm. Rectangular base with four receptacles. With the Arms of Dom Tomaz de Almeida. Marked *L* (Lisbon) and *MR*. Early XVIIIth Century.
Lent by the Museu de Arte Antiga, Lisbon.

208 **Bowl**
Silver. Diam. 39·5 cm. Plain silver, with shaped rim. Marked *L* (Lisbon) and *AM*. May be dated by the mark *c.* 1700.
Lent by the Fundação Ricardo Espirito Santo, Lisbon.

209 **A Salt**
Silver. H. 38·5 cm. The base of baluster form, in plain silver, surmounted by a canopy with a lion and the Arms of Sousa e Silva. Marked *B* (Braga) and *HSA*. Beginning of the XVIIIth Century.
Lent by the Viscondes de Paço de Nespereira, Braga.

210 **Two-handled Wine Cup**
Silver. Diam. 10·5 cm. Pineapple decoration. XVIIth Century.
Lent by Exmo. Sr. José Rosas J^{r.}, Oporto.

211 **Covered Jar (for Holy Oil)**
Silver. H. 38 cm. Dated *1682*. Of plain form and undecorated.
Lent by the Duques de Palmela, Lisbon.

212 **Salt-cellar**
Silver-gilt. H. 24·2 cm. Pyramidal shape, on three feet, decorated with acanthus. Marked *L* (Lisbon) and *IL*. Beginning of the XVIIIth Century.
Lent by the Fundação Ricardo Espirito Santo, Lisbon.

213 **Pair of Candlesticks**
Silver. H. 21 cm. On domed bases. Early XVIIth Century.
Lent by the Museu Machado de Castro, Coimbra.

214 **Salver on Foot**
Silver. Diam. 23 cm. With pineapple decoration. Similar to one bearing the hall-mark of Coimbra of the late XVIIth Century.
Lent by the Museu Machado de Castro, Coimbra.

215 **Dish**
Silver. Diam. 40·5 cm. Plain fluted style. Marked with a monogram *MG* (?). XVIIth Century.
Lent by Professor Reynaldo dos Santos, Lisbon.

216 **Incense Box in the shape of a Boat**
Silver. H. 15 cm.; L. 23 cm. Chased with acanthus. XVIIth Century.
Lent by the Museu de Arte Antiga, Lisbon.

217 **Ewer**
Silver. H. 27 cm. Helmet-shaped and with a female torso as a handle. XVIIth Century.
Lent by the Condes de Palma, Lisbon.

218 **Galleon**
Silver. H. 33 cm.; L. 30 cm. With an Angel figurehead. XVIIth Century.
Lent by the Museu de Arte Antiga, Lisbon.

219 **Two-handled Cup**
Silver. H. 9 cm. Plain, with snake handles. XVIIth Century.
Lent by Exmo. S^r. Luis Ferreira, Oporto.

220 **Dish**
Silver. Diam. 36 cm. Plain silver, fluted. Marked *P* (Porto) and *PR* (end of the XVIIth or beginning of the XVIIIth Century).
Lent by Professor Reynaldo dos Santos, Lisbon.

221 **Incense Box in the shape of a Boat**
Silver. L. 19·5 cm. Decorated with acanthus. Latter half of the XVIth Century.
Lent by the Museu Soares dos Reis, Oporto.

222 Ewer

Silver. H. 20 cm. Cylindrical form, undecorated, with harp-shaped handle. XVIIth Century.
Lent by the Palácio da Ajuda, Lisbon.

223 Ewer and Dish

Silver. (Ewer) H. 31·5 cm.; (Dish) L. 56 cm. Plain silver, gadrooned border. The handle of the ewer in the shape of a female figure. Period of Pedro II (1667–1706).
Lent by the Viscondes de Paço de Nespereira, Braga.

224 Two-handled Bowl

Silver. Diam. 25·5 cm. Lobed brim; embossed with flowers and leaves on the base. Style of the second half of the XVIIth Century. Marked *L* (Lisbon) and *ML*. Dated *1713*.
Lent by the Exmo. Sr. Francisco de Barros e Sá, Lisbon.

225 Altar Cruet and Stand

Silver. (Stand) L. 23 cm.; (Cruet) H. 11 cm. Undecorated and dated *1679*.
Lent by the Museu de Arte Antiga, Lisbon.

226 Inkstand with Bell

Silver. Diam. 28 cm. Five pieces and a tray. With the Arms of Bishop Frei Luis da Silva Telles (d. 1703). Marked *L* (Lisbon) and *MDO*. May be dated by the mark *c.* 1690.
Lent by the Museu d'Évora.

227 Ewer and Dish

Silver. (Ewer) H. 27 cm.; (Dish) Diam. 40 cm. The ewer of helmet shape, the dish with radiating compartments. Marked *L* (Lisbon) and *FD*. Early XVIIIth Century.
Lent by the Fundação Ricardo Espirito Santo, Lisbon.

228 Ewer

Silver-gilt. H. 29 cm. Helmet shape, the handle in the shape of a female figure. Late XVIIth Century.
Lent by the Museu de Lamego.

229 **Stoppered Bottle (for Holy Oil)**
Silver. H. 42·5 cm. Cylindrical form, undecorated. XVIIth Century.
Lent by the Sé d'Évora.

230 **Owl**
Silver. H. 13 cm. XVIIth Century. From the Convent of Santa Clara, Coimbra.
Lent by the Museu Machado de Castro, Coimbra.

231 **Owl**
Silver. H. 20 cm. Early XVIIth Century.
Lent by Comandante Ernesto de Vilhena, Lisbon.

232 **Pelican**
Silver. H. 17·5 cm. From the Convent of Santa Clara, Coimbra. XVIIth Century.
Lent by the Museu Machado de Castro, Coimbra.

233 **Bowl**
Silver. Diam. 34 cm. Plain silver, with shaped rim. Period of Pedro II (1667–1706).
Lent by the Palácio da Ajuda, Lisbon.

---

234 **Reredos**
Polychrome and gilded wood. H. 375 cm.: W. 320 cm. In the centre, the Virgin of the Immaculate Conception in prayer standing on the Moon and the Sun encircled by a Dragon; on the left the Holy Family, on the right a *Pietá*; framed in gilt wood pillars; in an arch above, the Annunciation and infant Angels. Mid-XVIIth Century. From the Church of Santa Clara, Coimbra.
Lent by the Museu Machado de Castro, Coimbra.

235 **Pair of two-handled Flower Vases**
Silver. H. 39 cm. Embossed with flowers. Given to the Cathedra of Coimbra in 1679.
Lent by the Museu Machado de Castro, Coimbra.

236 **Book Rest**

Pierced silver. H. 29 cm. L. 41 cm. Scroll decoration over velvet.
Late XVIIth Century.
Lent by the Museu de Guimarães.

237 **Missal Cover**

Chased silver on red velvet. L. 30 cm. With a Coat of Arms.
Second half of the XVIIth Century.
Lent by the Museu Alberto Sampaio, Guimarães.

238 **Pair of Candlesticks**

Silver. H. 49 cm. Chased with flat scrolls of stylised leaves. Early
XVIIth Century.
Lent by the Museu de Arte Antiga, Lisbon.

239 **Holy Water Stoup and Sprinkler**

Silver. H. 17 cm.; Diam. 21 cm. Engraved in Renaissance style.
End of the XVIth Century.
Lent by the Museu de Arte Antiga, Lisbon.

240 **Altar Cloth**

Gold tissue. 100 × 300 cm. The borders of red velvet, with scrolls
in bullion work. XVIth Century.
Lent by the Museu Machado de Castro, Coimbra.

241 **Bedspread**

Gold embroidery on red velvet. 288 × 214 cm. Oriental design.
XVIIth Century.
Lent by the Fundação Espirito Santo, Lisbon.

In Case J (Nos. 242–261)

242 **Dish**

Silver. Diam. 52 cm. Embossed with flowers, birds and foliage;
in the centre a Coat of Arms. Second half of the XVIIth Century.
Lent by the Exma. S^{ra.} Dona Amélia de Freitas G. Carvalho, Lisbon.

243 **Tazza**

Silver-gilt. Diam. 33 cm. Heavily decorated with flowers and
masks and the Arms of the Macedos family. Mid-XVIIth Century.
Lent by the Museu de Arte Antiga, Lisbon.

244 **Salver on Foot**

Silver. Diam. 30 cm. Chased with flowers between spiral lobes.
Marked *P* (Porto) and *R°*. Beginning of the XVIIIth Century.
Lent by the Victoria and Albert Museum, London.

245 **Pair of Candlesticks**

Silver-gilt. H. 52 cm. Gadrooned stems and heavy triangular bases.
Marked *L* (Lisbon) and *TC* (*c.* 1700–1720).
Lent by the Museu de Lamego.

246 **Dish**

Silver. Diam. 34 cm. Embossed with tulips and birds, a galleon in
the centre. Marked *L* (Lisbon) and *LS*. Late XVIIth Century.
Lent by Dr. José d'Alpuim, Viana do Castelo.

247 **Two-handled Bowl**

Silver. Diam. 24·5 cm. Decorated with spiral lobes centering on a
cockle-shell. Marked *P* (Porto) and *AC*. Period of Pedro II (1667–
1706).
*Lent by Exmo· S^r· and S^ra· Engenheiro Pedro Inácio Alvares Ribeiro,
Oporto.*

248 **Bowl**

Silver. Diam. 32 cm. Embossed with flowers and leaves; in the
centre a basket of fruit. Second half of the XVIIth Century.
Lent by Exma· S^ra· Dona Amélia de Freitas G. Carvalho, Lisbon.

249 **Incense Box in the shape of a Boat**

Silver. H. 16·5 cm.; L. 21 cm. XVIIth Century.
Lent by the Museu de Arte Antiga, Lisbon.

250 **Two Incense Burners**

Silver-gilt. H. 18 cm. Pyramidal form, gadrooned, and decorated
with acanthus on the triangular base. Period of Pedro II (1667–1706).
Lent by the Museu de Lamego.

251 **Deep Dish with double indentation**

Silver. L. 56·5 cm. The border embossed with flowers, birds and
fruit. Mid-XVIIth Century.
Lent by the Viscondes de Paço de Nespereira, Braga.

252 Ewer

Parcel-gilt. H. 36 cm. Helmet-shaped, decorated with bands of foliage. XVIIth Century.
Lent by the Fundação Ricardo Espirito Santo, Lisbon.

253 Incense Box in the shape of a Boat

Silver. L. 25 cm. Engraved with acanthus, and with a lion figure-head. Marked *B* (Beja) and *F* (or *E*) *VD*. Early XVIIIth Century in the style of the XVIIth.
Lent by the Museu Soares dos Reis, Oporto.

254 Ewer and Dish

Silver. (Ewer) H. 33 cm.; (Dish) Diam. 48·5 cm. Embossed with tulips, birds and acanthus. Marked *L* (Lisbon) and *VR*. Beginning of the XVIIIth Century.
Lent by the Museu de S. Roque, Lisbon.

255 Casket

Tortoise-shell and silver. L. 23·5 cm. XVIIth Century.
Lent by the Museu Soares dos Reis, Oporto.

256 Two-handled Bowl

Silver. Diam. 14·5 cm. Lobed brim, chased with flowers and leaves below. Marked *P* (Porto) and *M* (end of the XVIIth Century or beginning of the XVIIIth).
Lent by the Exmo. Sr. António Russel de Sousa, Oporto.

257 Dish

Silver. Diam. 25·8 cm. Embossed with tulips and, in the centre, a flower-head. Second half of the XVIIth Century.
Lent by Exma. S^{ra.} Dona Amélia de Freitas G. Carvalho, Lisbon.

258 Dish

Silver. Diam. 32 cm. Embossed with tulips and, in the centre, a peacock. Second half of the XVIIth Century.
Lent by Dr. Cassiano Neves, Lisbon.

259 Tazza

Silver. Diam. 27 cm. Marked *L* (Lisbon) and *DM*. Early XVIIIth Century in the style of the XVIIth.
Lent by Professor Reynaldo dos Santos, Lisbon.

260 Salver

Silver-gilt. Diam. 19 cm. The border decorated with leaves, peacocks and the rim with a frieze of acanthus. Mid-XVIIth Century. *Lent by Dr. Augusto Lamas, Lisbon.*

261 Large Dish

Silver. Diam. 53 cm. Embossed with birds, animals and flowers. Marked *L* (Lisbon) and *AS*. Late XVIIth Century. *Lent by the Victoria and Albert Museum, London.*

262 High-backed Chair

Walnut, with embossed leather seat and back, and decorated with brass nails. H. 127 cm. XVIIIth Century. *Lent by the Museu-Biblioteca Conde Castro Guimarães, Cascais.*

263 Small Tabernacle

Gilded wood. H. 55 cm. Decorated with scrolls in Baroque style and enshrining a statuette in painted terracotta of the Virgin and Child. Late XVIIth Century. *Lent by the Museu de Aveiro.*

264 Small Bedstead

Lignum vitae. The posts of turned bobbins and spirals, the head and foot elaborately carved and with turned finials. Damask canopy. L. 190 cm. XVIIth Century. *Lent by the Fundação Ricardo Espirito Santo, Lisbon.*

265 Bedspread

White linen with coloured silk embroidery. 241 × 173 cm. Vases of flowers and parrots. XVIIIth Century. Castelo Branco style. *Lent by the Museu de Arte Antiga, Lisbon.*

266 Arraiolos Carpet

Wool embroidery. 270 × 225 cm. Design with Persian influence, in blue, yellow and brown. XVIIth Century. *Lent by the Fundação Ricardo Espirito Santo, Lisbon.*

JOSEPHA DE OBIDOS (1634–1684)

267 Still Life

Canvas. 84 × 160 cm. Dated *1676*. Josepha de Obidos was the daughter of a painter. Many of her works were commissioned by convents.
Lent by the Museu-Biblioteca de Santarem.

268 Chest

Lignum vitae. H. 77 cm.: W. 67 cm.: L. 117 cm. XVIIth Century.
Lent by the Museu de Arte Antiga, Lisbon.

269 Oil Lamp with four Burners

Silver. H. 58 cm. Octagonal base and baluster stem. Plain silver, with the Arms of Almeidas (or Melos), Pereiras, Sampaio e Sousa Prado (with an episcopal hat). Marked *L* (Lisbon) and *AA* (*c.* 1700–1720).
Lent by Dr. Manuel de Velasco Bachá da Cunha Santiago, Lisbon.

270 Basin

Faience. Diam. 47 cm. Decorated in blue with Renaissance-style masks in relief, flowers and birds. Lisbon, XVIIth Century.
Lent by the Museu de Arte Antiga, Lisbon.

271 Flat-sided Armorial Bottle

Faience. H. 35·5 cm. With the Arms of the Order of St. Domingos. Lisbon, XVIIth Century.
Lent by the Museu de Arte Antiga, Lisbon.

272 Two Angels (Candle-holders)

Gilded wood. H. 88 cm. Early XVIIIth Century.
Lent by the Church of Arouca.

273 Pair of Plinths

Gilded wood. H. 167 cm. Carved and decorated in late Renaissance style. XVIIth Century.
Lent by the Museu Machado de Castro, Coimbra.

274 **Chair**

Walnut and embossed leather. Brass studs and finials. H. 137 cm.
First half of the XVIIth Century.
Lent by the Museu de Arte Antiga, Lisbon.

275 **Chest**

Vinhatico (a species of mahogany) with mouldings of lignum vitae.
H. 94 cm.: W. 72 cm.: L. 164 cm. XVIIth Century.
Lent by the Museu de Arte Antiga, Lisbon.

276 **Drug Jar**

Faience. H. 26·8 cm. Decorated with exotic birds and flowers in
blue. Lisbon, XVIIth Century.
Lent by the Museu Soares dos Reis, Oporto.

277 **Dish**

Faience. Diam. 40·2 cm. Decorated with a deer and flowers in blue.
Lent by the Museu Machado de Castro, Coimbra.

278 **Punch Bowl and Cover**

Faience. Diam. 35·5 cm. Decorated with figures, animals and
trees in blue and manganese. Lisbon, XVIIth Century.
Lent by the Museu de Arte Antiga, Lisbon.

279 **Armorial Dish**

Faience. Diam. 37 cm. Chinese-style designs on the rim, and the
Arms of the Costas family in the centre. Lisbon, XVIIth Century.
Lent by the Museu de Arte Antiga, Lisbon.

280 **Drug Jar**

Faience. H. 27·5 cm. Decorated with birds and flowers in blue
and manganese. Lisbon, XVIIth Century.
Lent by the Museu Soares dos Reis, Oporto.

JOSEFA DE OBIDOS (1634–1684)

281 **Still Life**

Canvas. 84 × 160 cm. Dated *1676*.
Lent by the Museu-Biblioteca de Santarem.

GALLERY V

282 Arraiolos Carpet
Wool embroidery. 279 × 226 cm. Portuguese folk-design with animals in polychrome. Early XVIIIth Century. From the Monastery of São Bento, Évora.
Lent by the Museu de Arte Antiga, Lisbon.

282a Arraiolos Carpet
Wool embroidery. 232 × 150 cm. Oriental design in polychrome. Early XVIIIth Century. From the Monastery of Paraíso, Évora.
Lent by the Museu de Arte Antiga, Lisbon.

283 Bedspread
Yellow silk with coloured embroidery. 273 × 215 cm. A double-headed eagle and hunting scenes. Indo-Portuguese work, XVIIth Century.
Lent by the Museu de Arte Antiga, Lisbon.

In Case K (Nos. 284–304)

284 Dish
Faience. Diam. 38·3 cm. Decorated with birds and animals in blue and manganese and inscribed on the rim: *GAMA*. Lisbon, XVIIth Century.
Lent by the Museu Machado de Castro, Coimbra.

285 Armorial Platter
Faience. Diam. 26·7 cm. With the Arms of Portugal in blue, in the centre. Lisbon, XVIIth Century.
Lent by the Museu de Arte Antiga, Lisbon.

286 Dish
Faience. Diam. 37·6 cm. Decorated on the rim with Chinese symbols and inscribed in the centre: *RIBEIRO*. Lisbon, XVIIth Century.
Lent by the Museu Machado de Castro, Coimbra.

287 Dish
Faience. Diam. 27·6 cm. Decorated in blue and white with, in the centre, a Portuguese lady in contemporary costume. Lisbon, XVIIth Century.
Lent by the Museu Soares dos Reis, Oporto.

288 Jar

Faience. H. 32 cm. Decorated with parrots and flowers in blue and manganese. Lisbon, XVIIth Century.
Lent by the Museu de Arte Antiga, Lisbon.

289 Dish

Faience. Diam. 40·7 cm. Stylised foliage on the rim and a female head in the centre. Lisbon, XVIIth Century.
Lent by the Museu de Arte Antiga, Lisbon.

290 Pear-shaped Pitcher

Faience. H. 29 cm. With the Cross and Three Nails in blue monochrome. Lisbon, beginning of the XVIIth Century.
Lent by the Museu Soares dos Reis, Oporto.

291 Armorial Dish

Faience. Diam. 33 cm. The Arms of the Silvas family in blue and manganese. Inscribed on the reverse side and dated: *Agostinho de Paiva—1694.* Coimbra, XVIIth Century.
Lent by the Museu Soares dos Rios, Oporto.

292 Four-handled Jar

Faience. H. 31 cm. Decorated with Chinese figures, animals and scrolls, in late Ming style. Lisbon, XVIIth Century.
Lent by the Museu de Arte Antiga, Lisbon.

293 High-necked Armorial Bottle

Faience. H. 24·1 cm. With the Arms of Portugal and the date *1641.* Made in Lisbon.
Lent by the Museu Soares dos Reis, Oporto.

294 Dish

Faience. Diam. 40 cm. The rim decorated in blue in late Ming style, a Portuguese figure in the costume of 1640 in the centre. Lisbon, XVIIth Century.
Lent by the Museu de Arte Antiga, Lisbon.

295 High-necked Armorial Bottle

Faience. H. 24 cm. With the Arms of Portugal and the date *1641.* Lisbon, XVIIth Century.
Lent by the Museu Machado de Castro, Coimbra.

3   65

296 Dish

Faience. Diam. 35 cm. Decorated with Chinese figures and
Oriental symbols.   Lisbon, XVIIth Century.
Lent by the Museu de Arte Antiga, Lisbon.

297 Jar

Faience. H. 34 cm. Decorated with rabbits and flowers, scrolls on
the shoulder. Lisbon, XVIIth Century.
Lent by the Museu de Arte Antiga, Lisbon.

298 Armorial Dish

Faience. Diam. 37·5 cm. Lace-design decoration on the rim and the
Arms of the Sisterhood of Saint Isabel. XVIIth Century. From
the Convent of Santa Clara, Coimbra.
Lent by the Museu de Arte Antiga, Lisbon.

299 Dish

Faience. Diam. 33·8 cm. Fluted shape and decorated in blue with
a Cupid in the centre. Coimbra, Brioso ware. Late XVIIth
Century.
Lent by the Museu Machado de Castro, Coimbra.

300 Dish

Faience. Diam. 39·2 cm. With Oriental decoration on the rim and
centre. Lisbon, XVIIth Century.
Lent by the Museu de Arte Antiga, Lisbon.

301 Dish

Faience. Diam. 38·7 cm. Decorated with deer, a Chinese figure,
and Episcopal Arms. Lisbon, XVIIth Century.
Lent by the Museu Machado de Castro, Coimbra.

302 Fluted Bowl

Faience. Diam. 26 cm. Inscribed: *MENEZES* in blue and
manganese. Coimbra, late XVIIth Century.
Lent by the Museu Machado de Castro, Coimbra.

303 Armorial Dish

Faience. Diam. 28·2 cm. Oriental decoration on the rim and
the Arms of the Barbosas family in the centre. Lisbon, XVIIth
Century.
Lent by the Museu de Arte Antiga, Lisbon.

304 **Pear-shaped Pitcher**
Faience. H. 24 cm. Decorated with a bird in blue. Lisbon, beginning of XVIIth Century.
Lent by the Museu Soares dos Reis, Oporto.

---

305 **Chair**
Chestnut, with embossed leather back and seat. H. 97 cm. First half of the XVIIth Century.
Lent by the Museu de Arte Antiga, Lisbon.

306 **Altar Frontal of Tiles (Azulejos)**
Decorated with flowers and birds in polychrome, the border in Renaissance style. 84×181 cm. Early XVIIth Century.
Lent by the Museu Machado de Castro, Coimbra.

DOMINGOS VIEIRA (Active 1627–1652)
307 **Gonçalo de Sousa de Macedo**
Canvas. 204 × 98 cm.
Lent by Maestro Pedro de Freitas Branco.

308 **Part of an Altar**
Gilded wood, heavily carved, the supporting salomonic pillars wreathed with vines, the sides with pelicans and foliage, the frieze of the capitals with polychrome cherub heads. H. 251 cm. Late XVIIth Century.
Lent by the Museu Machado de Castro, Coimbra.

309 **A Pelican**
Gilded wood. H. 58 cm. XVIIIth Century.
Lent by the Museu de Arouca.

310 **Panel of Tiles (Azulejos)**
Bold decoration of birds and flowers in polychrome. 73 × 56 cm. XVIIth Century. Northern Portuguese style.
Lent by the Museu de Guimarães.

311 **Altar Frontal of Tiles (Azulejos)**
Decorated with birds, flowers and a pagoda in polychrome. 106×176 cm. XVIIth Century.
Lent by the Museu Machado de Castro, Coimbra.

DOMINGOS VIEIRA (Active 1627–1652)

312 Dona Margarida Moreira

Canvas. 204 × 100 cm. The wife of Gonçalo de Sousa de Macedo (see No. 307).

Lent by Maestro Pedro de Freitas Branco.

313 Chair

Walnut, with embossed leather back and seat, decorated with brass studs. H. 41 cm. XVIIth Century.

Lent by the Museu de Aveiro.

313a Chair

Lignum vitae. The seat and back of chased leather. Brass studs and finials. H. 124 cm. XVIIth Century.

Lent by the Fundação Ricardo Espirito Santo, Lisbon.

314 Bedspread

White linen embroidered with yellow and pink silk. 290 × 209 cm. Representing the Five Senses, with inscriptions in Portuguese. Indo-Portuguese work, mid-XVIIth Century.

Lent by the Museu de Arte Antiga, Lisbon

In Case L (Nos. 315–341)

315 Armorial Bowl

Faience. H. 12 cm.: Diam. 22 cm. With the Arms of the Carneiros family. Lisbon, XVIIth Century.

Lent by the Museu de Arte Antiga, Lisbon.

316 Dish

Faience. Diam. 39·2 cm. With Buddhistic symbols on the rim and in the centre an equestrian figure of the XVIIth Century. Lisbon, XVIIth Century.

Lent by the Museu Machado de Castro, Coimbra.

317 Octagonal Tazza

Faience. H. 8 cm.: Diam. 23·5 cm. Decorated with cherub masks in relief and the Arms of the Limas family in blue. Lisbon, XVIIth Century.

Lent by the Museu de Arte Antiga, Lisbon.

318 Bottle

Faience. Diam. 27·5 cm. Decorated with birds and flowers in blue and manganese. Lisbon, XVIIth Century.
Lent by the Museu de Arte Antiga, Lisbon.

319 Dish

Faience. Diam. 40·8 cm. With Oriental subjects in polychrome on the rim, and the Sacrifice of Abraham in the centre. Lisbon, XVIIth Century.
Lent by the Museu de Arte Antiga, Lisbon.

320 Toilet Box

Faience. H. 22 cm. Lobed shape with Oriental decoration. Lisbon, XVIIth Century.
Lent by the Museu de Arte Antiga, Lisbon.

321 Two-handled Bowl

Faience. Diam. 13 cm. Arabesques in blue. Lisbon, XVIIth Century.
Lent by the Museu Soares dos Reis, Oporto.

322 Two-handled Armorial Jar

Faience. H. 30·5 cm. Decorated with Chinoiserie figures and the Arms of the Bareto e Lima families. Lisbon, XVIIth Century.
Lent by the Museu de Arte Antiga, Lisbon.

323 Flat-sided Bottle

Faience. H. 25 cm. Decorated with birds in blue and manganese. Lisbon, XVIIth Century.
Lent by the Museu de Arte Antiga, Lisbon.

324 Plate

Faience. Diam. 22·2 cm. Decorated in blue and manganese with flowers in the centre and scale and key-fret on the rim. Lisbon, XVIIth Century.
Lent by the Museu de Arte Antiga, Lisbon.

325 Oval Dish

Faience. Max. diam. 21·2 cm. Decorated with lace design in blue and manganese. Lisbon, XVIIth Century.
Lent by the Museu Machado de Castro, Coimbra.

326 Pot

Faience. H. 30·5 cm. Decorated with floral trellis work. Lisbon, XVIIth Century.
Lent by the Museu de Arte Antiga, Lisbon.

327 Dish

Faience. Diam. 41 cm. With the figure of Bathsheba in the centre, and on the reverse side the inscription and date: *D Inês, 1660.* Lisbon, XVIIth Century.
Lent by the Museu de Arte Antiga, Lisbon.

328 Flat-sided Bottle

Faience. H. 26·5 cm. Decorated with a lion and equestrian figure in blue. Lisbon, XVIIth Century.
Lent by the Fundação da Casa de Bragança, Vila Viçosa.

329 Basin

Faience. Diam. 38·5 cm. Decorated with Chinese subjects, deer and a palm tree in the centre. Lisbon, XVIIth Century.
Lent by the Museu de Arte Antiga, Lisbon.

330 Dish

Faience. Diam. 39·3 cm. Decorated in Chinese style. Lisbon, XVIIth Century.
Lent by the Museu de Arte Antiga, Lisbon.

331 Pitcher

Faience. Diam. 37 cm. With mythological figures, animals and borders in Oriental style. Lisbon, XVIIth Century.
Lent by the Museu de Arte Antiga, Lisbon.

332 Dish

Faience. Diam. 40·5 cm. With decoration in polychrome of Oriental inspiration, and the Arms of Dom Pedro de Almeida, Viceroy of Portuguese India, in the centre. Lisbon, XVIIIth Century.
Lent by the Museu de Arte Antiga, Lisbon.

333 Tazza

Faience. H. 50 cm.: Diam. 19·5 cm. In the centre a winged heart and the inscription: *AMOR.* Lisbon, XVIIth Century.
Lent by the Museu de Arte Antiga, Lisbon.

334 Oval Dish

Faience. Diam. 22·8 cm. Decorated with lace pattern in blue and manganese. Lisbon, XVIIth Century.
Lent by the Museu Soares dos Reis, Oporto.

335 Two-handled Armorial Porringer

Faience. H. 6·4 cm. With the Arms of the Silvas family in blue and manganese. Lisbon, XVIIth Century.
Lent by the Museu Machado de Castro, Coimbra.

336 Octagonal Tazza

Faience. Diam. 26·5 cm. Polychrome, the rim decorated with cherubs in relief, showing the influence of Italian majolica. Lisbon, XVIIth Century.
Lent by the Museu de Arte Antiga, Lisbon.

337 Armorial Dish

Faience. Diam. 19·4 cm. With the Arms of the Silvas family in blue. Lisbon, XVIIth Century.
Lent by the Museu Machado de Castro, Coimbra.

338 Octagonal Bowl

Faience. H. 8·5 cm.: Diam. 18·5 cm. Geometrical decoration. Lisbon, XVIIth Century.
Lent by the Museu de Arte Antiga, Lisbon.

339 Dish

Faience. Diam. 37 cm. With Fortune in the centre and Chinese aster-pattern on the rim. Lisbon, XVIIth Century.
Lent by the Museu de Arte Antiga, Lisbon.

340 Two-handled Jar

Faience. H. 22·7 cm. Decorated in blue and inscribed: *Mjchaella.* XVIIIth Century.
Lent by the Museu Machado de Castro, Coimbra.

341 Bowl

Faience. Diam. 21·5 cm. Decorated with flowers and fruits in blue, showing Oriental influence. Dated *1621.* Probably made in Lisbon.
Lent by the Museu Soares dos Reis, Oporto.

342   Panel of Tiles (Azulejos)
In blue and yellow.   60 × 90 cm.   XVIIth Century.
Lent by the Museu d'Évora.

343   Tabernacle
Carved and gilded wood.   H. 172 cm.   Decorated with cherubs in polychrome.   A statuette of St. Anne in painted wood in the niche.
XVIIth Century.
Lent by the Museu de Aveiro.

DIRK STOOP (1610–1686)
344   Catharine of Braganza
Canvas.   150 × 100 cm.   The original portrait, at present unidentified, of which this is one of several versions, was probably painted before Catharine's marriage treaty in June, 1661.   The old-fashioned style of the dress (hooped skirts had gone out in England 30 years earlier) to which Catharine clung for some time after her arrival caused considerable comment.   Dirk Stoop came to England in the retinue of the Infanta; he had previously worked in Lisbon for several years.
Lent by the National Portrait Gallery, London.

345   Arraiolos Carpet
Wool embroidery.   229 × 138 cm.   Persian design in polychrome.
Late XVIIth Century.
Lent by the Museu de Arte Antiga, Lisbon.

346   Cabinet on Stand
Lignum vitae.   H. 146 cm.: W. 49 cm.: L. 93 cm.   The drawers coffered and brass-mounted, the corners with Renaissance-style pillars, the stand elaborately turned and with an apron of *amorini* and foliage.
XVIIth Century.
Lent by the Museu de Arte Antiga, Lisbon.

347   Pot
Faience.   H. 22·5 cm.   Decorated with birds and flowers in blue and manganese.   Lisbon, XVIIth Century.
Lent by the Museu Machado de Castro, Coimbra.

348 **Arm Chair**
Lignum vitae. H. 109 cm. The arm-rests carved with masks, the seat and back covered with red velvet; brass studs and finials. XVIIth Century.
Lent by the Museu de Arouca.

349 **A Saint's Vision**
Polychrome and gilded wood. H. 92 cm. XVIIth Century.
Lent by the Museu Machado de Castro, Coimbra.

350 **Table**
Lignum vitae. H. 74 cm.; W. 105 cm.; L. 168 cm. The top with spiral mouldings, the legs and stretchers turned. XVIIth Century.
Lent by the Museu de Arte Antiga, Lisbon.

351 **Tazza**
Silver. Diam. 24 in. Embossed with flowers and foliage. Marked P (Porto) and MF. End of the XVIIth Century.
Lent by Dr. José d'Alpuim, Viana do Castelo.

352 **Dish**
Faience. Diam. 39 cm. Decorated in blue with animals and flowers in Chinese late Ming style. XVIIth Century.
Lent by the Museu de Arte Antiga, Lisbon.

353 **Armorial Jar with flattened sides**
Faience. H. 29·5 cm. With the Arms of Queen Luisa de Gusmão. Lisbon, XVIIth Century.
Lent by the Museu de Arte Antiga, Lisbon.

354 **Mace**
Silver, chased. H. 97 cm. With an armillary sphere as finial. First half of the XVIIth Century.
Lent by the Museu de S. Roque, Lisbon.

355 **Dish**
Silver. Diam. 35 cm. Chased with stylised leaves in panels, the rim serrated with cockle-shells. *c.* 1600.
Lent by the Museu dos Soares Reis, Oporto.

*356   Lectern

Lignum vitae.   H. 188 cm.   With floral and scroll decoration in brass.   XVIIth Century.
Lent by the Museu de Arte Antiga, Lisbon.

*357   Book-cover

Pierced silver on red velvet, the silver worked with a medallion of the Virgin and Child surrounded by flowers and foliage.   H. 36 cm. Marked *P* (Porto) and *RLO*.   End of XVIIth Century.
Lent by the Sé do Porto

In the Doorway

358 Lamp

Silver and bronze.   Faceted triangular form with Angels holding the three chains framed with stems of leaves.   Second quarter of the XVIIIth Century.
Lent by the Museu Machado de Castro, Coimbra.

*Numbers 356 and 357 transferred to Gallery VI

GALLERY VI

359 Secretaire Cabinet

Wood, japanned in red and gold; the cabinet surmounted by a "broken" pediment. First half of XVIIIth Century. Inside the cabinet, a statuette of the Virgin and Child in terracotta, of earlier style.
Lent by the Museu de Aveiro.

360 Armorial Chair

Lignum vitae with seat of embossed leather, the splat carved with a Coat of Arms. H. 114 cm. Middle of the XVIIIth Century.
Lent by the Museu de Arte Antiga, Lisbon.

361 Bedspread

Linen, embroidered with coloured silks. 203 × 280 cm. Floral decoration. XVIIIth Century.
Lent by the Museu Machado de Castro, Coimbra.

362 Altar Frontal

Silk brocade. 92 × 175 cm. The border of velvet embroidered in gilt and silver. XVIIth Century.
Lent by the Museu de Aveiro.

363 Bedstead

Lignum vitae. Turned and fluted posts, the head carved with scrolls in rococo style. Panel and canopy of red damask. L. 194 cm. Middle of the XVIIIth Century.
Lent by the Fundação Ricardo Espirito Santo, Lisbon.

364 Bedspread

Linen, embroidered with red silk. 240 × 140 cm. Decorated with tulips and other flowers in the style of Castelo Branco. XVIIIth Century.
Lent by the Museu Machado de Castro, Coimbra.

365 Folding Chair

Lignum vitae. Seat of embossed leather, and studded with nails. H. 93 cm. Middle of the XVIIIth Century.
Lent by the Fundação Ricardo Espirito Santo, Lisbon.

366 Chest of Drawers
Lignum vitae. Drawers with panels in lighter wood. Canted corners. The carved scrolls and metal mounts in rococo style. H. 80 cm.: W. 83 cm. Middle of the XVIIIth Century.
Lent by the Fundação Ricardo Espirito Santo, Lisbon.

367 Decanter
Porcelain. H. 26 cm. With a view of the Vista Alegre works in sepia on a white background. Vista Alegre ware. Early XIXth Century.
Lent by Dr. J. Cid dos Santos, Lisbon.

368 Ewer and Basin
Silver. (Ewer) H. 29·5 cm.; (Bowl) L. 41 cm. The Ewer helmet-shaped, the Basin with shaped edge chased in the style of John V. Marked *L* (Lisbon) and *AM* (1720–*c.* 1750).
Lent by the Fundação Ricardo Espirito Santo, Lisbon.

369 Candlestick
Silver. H. 23 cm. Spiral fluting with diminishing beads. Second half of the XVIIIth Century.
Lent by the Fundação Ricardo Espirito Santo, Lisbon.

370 Arraiolos Carpet
Wool embroidery. 386 × 218 cm. Decorated with birds, flowers and double-headed eagles in blue and brown. XVIIth Century.
Lent by the Fundação Ricardo Espirito Santo, Lisbon.

DOMINGOS ANTÓNIO DE SEQUEIRA (1768–1837)
371 The Virgin and Child
Canvas. 48 × 39 cm. Painted *c.* 1825. From the Ameal Collection.
Lent by the Museu de Arte Antiga, Lisbon.

372 Bedspread
Painted linen, embroidered with white silk. 270 × 170 cm. Floral decoration. XVIIIth Century.
Lent by the Museu Machado de Castro, Coimbra.

373 Folding Chair

Lignum vitae. Back and seat in embossed leather with metal nails, and with a Coat of Arms in the centre. H. 118 cm. XVIIIth Century.
Lent by the Fundação Ricardo Espirito Santo, Lisbon.

374 Quadruple-top Games Table

Lignum vitae. Inlaid with kingwood and satinwood, the flaps with ivory, the work of exceptional quality. On four slender legs; one leg hinged to support the different table-tops, three of which are for various games and the fourth for use as a dressing-table. The legs and apron are delicately carved, the drawers silver-mounted. H. 72 cm.: Diam.: 103 cm. Middle of the XVIIIth Century.
Lent by the Fundação Ricardo Espirito Santo, Lisbon.

PORTUGUESE SCHOOL (Early XVIIIth Century)

375 Portrait of a Young Nobleman

Canvas. 73 × 57 cm.
Lent by Professor Reynaldo dos Santos, Lisbon.

DOMINGOS ANTÓNIO DE SEQUEIRA (1768–1837)

376 Dr. Neves

Canvas. 40 × 31·8 cm. Signed and dated *1825* and inscribed with the sitter's name on the stretcher. Coll: P. M. Turner; Lit. *Burlington Magazine*, Vol. LXXIV, p. 153 (repr.).
Lent by the Ashmolean Museum, Oxford.

377 Armchair

Walnut. H. 103 cm. Carved with scroll work and other rococo motives; cabriole legs. XVIIIth Century.
Lent by Engº. H. Chaves, Lisbon.

378 Four-chair Settee

Lignum vitae. Carved with rococo scroll work, the seat and back of leather incised in a similar style; serpentine seat-rail; cabriole legs. H. 105 cm.: W. 216 cm. Middle of the XVIIIth Century.
Lent by the Fundação Ricardo Espirito Santo, Lisbon.

379 Armchair

Lignum vitae. Serpentine seat-rail, cabriole legs. Carved in rococo style and upholstered in red velvet. H. 102 cm. Third quarter of the XVIIIth Century.
Lent by the Duques de Palmela, Lisbon.

380 **Oriental Bedspread**

Blue satin embroidered in gold. 330 × 274 cm. In the centre, a double-headed eagle. Woven in the Far East for the Portuguese market. XVIIth Century.

Lent by the Museu de Arte Antiga, Lisbon.

381 **Shrine on Secretaire Base**

Wood, japanned in various colours and gilt. H. 247 cm.; W. 174 cm. The shrine carved and gilded with rococo ornament; the inside mouldings of the doors frame painted scenes of the Passion. Mid-XVIIIth Century. Traditionally supposed to have been part of the furniture of a ship.

Lent by the Fábrica de Vista Alegre.

382 **Chair**

Lignum vitae. High-backed, with damask seat. Carved in rococo style. H. 113 cm. Third quarter of the XVIIIth Century.

Lent by the Fundação Ricardo Espirito Santo, Lisbon.

DOMINGOS ANTÓNIO DE SEQUEIRA (1768–1837)

383 **General Beresford**

Pencil. 51 × 36 cm. May be dated *c.* 1817.

Lent by the Museu de Arte Antiga, Lisbon.

DOMINGOS ANTÓNIO DE SEQUEIRA (1768–1837)

384 **Allegory of the Return of King John VI**

Canvas. 48 × 65 cm. Painted *c.* 1815.

Lent by the Duques de Palmela, Lisbon.

DOMINGOS ANTONIO DE SEQUEIRA (1768–1837)

385 **Sketch of the Artist**

Pen and ink. 32 × 24 cm. A drawing made in reply to an invitation from the Marquez de Borba. It represents the artist in his studio surrounded by his models for the Service presented by the Regent John VI to the Duke of Wellington (see Nos. 396–8). The letter which he holds in his hand is dated August 1813. It declines the invitation on the grounds of his pre-occupation with this commission.

Lent by Dr. Pedro Batalha Reis, Lisbon.

386 **Table with two Drawers**

Lignum vitae. H. 82 cm. On cabriole legs, the serpentine front centring in an apron with a satyr mask. Carved with scrolls and masks in rococo style. Mid-XVIIIth Century.
Lent by Exma. S^ra. Olagabal, Oporto.

387 **Pair of Candlesticks**

Silver. H. 23·2 cm. Decorated with spiral fluting; engraved base. Marked *EV* (Évora) and *ANS* (Antonio Nunes da Silva). The mark registered in 1769.
Lent by the Fundação Ricardo Espirito Santo, Lisbon.

388 **Small Ewer**

Silver. H. 17·5 cm. Rococo decoration, with masks and a Chinese head on the handle. The Arms of Sousa, Silva, Freire and Alte. Mid-XVIIIth Century.
Lent by the Marqueses de Sá da Bandeira, Lisbon.

389 **Basin**

Silver. Diam. 27 cm. The edge engraved with lappets in the King John V style. In the centre the Arms of Sousa, Silva, Freire, and Alte.
Lent by the Marqueses de Sá de Bandeira, Lisbon.

390 **Knife-box**

Lignum vitae. H. 13·5 cm. Richly carved *en rocaille* and of delicately shaped form; silver mount. XVIIIth Century.
Lent by the Museu Soares dos Reis, Oporto.

391 **Arraiolos Carpet**

Wool embroidery. 230 × 128 cm. Geometric design in blue and yellow. XVIIth Century. From the Monastery of Paraíso, Évora.
Lent by the Museu de Arte Antiga, Lisbon.

392 **Bedspread**

Red silk with polychrome embroidery. 255 × 194 cm. Representing the Five Senses, with double-headed eagles and peacocks. Indo-Portuguese work, XVIIth Century.
Lent by the Museu-Biblioteca Castro Guimarães, Cascais.

393 Coffee-pot

Silver. H. 29·5 cm. Flattened oval shape; a monkey finial. Marked
L (Lisbon) and illegible letters. Neo-classic style. *c.* 1804–1812.
Lent by the Fundação Ricardo Espirito Santo, Lisbon.

394 Two Altar Vessels

Silver. H. 43 cm. Fluted canister shape; silver-gilt urn finials.
The Arms of Dom João de Magalhães e Avellar, Bishop of Oporto.
Marked P (Porto) and IOC (1810–1818). Neo-classic style.
Lent by the Museu Soares dos Reis, Oporto.

395 Ewer and Shaving Bowl

Silver. (Ewer) H. 29 cm.; (Bowl) L. 43·5 cm. The Ewer of flattened
oval form, with the Arms of Queen Maria I. Marked L (Lisbon) and
AFC (Antonio Firmo da Costa—registered in 1793). Neo-classic
style.
*Lent by the Museu Soares dos Reis, Oporto (by courtesy of the Ministério
das Finanças).*

396 Triangular Covered Dish

Parcel-gilt. Each side, 28 cm. The dish decorated with a band of
laurels, the cover with the Arms of the Duke of Wellington. Pineapple handle. From the same service as No. 398.
Lent by the Duke of Wellington, London.

397 Tureen

Parcel-gilt. Diam. 41 cm. Circular form, supported by mermaids.
From the same service as No. 398 and with similar decoration.
Lent by the Duke of Wellington, London.

398 Large Tureen

Parcel-gilt. L. 55 cm. Oval form, with bands of laurel leaves and
swags and the Arms of the Duke of Wellington, supported by four
mermaids. Pineapple handle. From the service given by the Prince
Regent John VI to the Duke of Wellington in 1816. The service
was made in Lisbon from 1811–1816 from designs by the painter
Domingos António de Sequeira. It comprises more than one thousand
pieces. An important part of the service is exhibited at Apsley
House.
Lent by the Duke of Wellington, London.

399 Coffee-pot
Silver. H. 32 cm. Flattened octangular base, on four small feet.
Vase finial. Neo-classic style. Late XVIIIth Century.
Lent by Visconde da Trindade, Lisbon.

400 Ewer and Shaving Bowl
Silver. (Ewer) H. 32 cm.; (Bowl) L. 50 cm. Fluted decoration.
Marked *P* (Porto) and *BM*. Neo-classic style. 1792–1810.
Lent by the Visconde da Trindade, Lisbon.

401 Covered Dish
Silver. L. 25 cm. Rectangular shape on four ball-feet with dolphins
on the lid and engraved with bands of laurel leaves. Neo-classic
style. Marked *L* (Lisbon) and *ANT* (Alexandre Norberto Torres,
registered 1812).
Lent by Ex^(ma.) S^(ra.) Dona Amélia de Freitas G. Carvalho, Lisbon.

---

402 Pair of Archways
Gilded wood deeply carved, supported by twin pairs of salomonic
pillars wreathed with vines, amongst them birds eating the grapes;
the bases, friezes and arches with cherub-heads in polychrome, the
arches heavily carved with similar motifs. H. 343 cm.: W. 225 cm.
Late XVIIth or early XVIIIth Century.
Lent by the Convento de Jesus, Aveiro.

403 A Pair of Azulejos (Tiled) Panels
H. 2 m. 20: W. 90 cm. In blues and white: *amorini* support an
elaborate baroque structure surmounted by a fantastic mask: vista of
trees, birds and landscape. XVIIIth Century, style of King John V.
Lent by the Museu de Aveiro.

404 Covered Jar
Silver. H. 50 cm. Of bulbous form with engraving of foliage on
neck and lid. *P* (Porto) and *RC* (1768–1792).
Lent by the Museu de Lamego.

405 Two Baroque Angels
Polychrome and gilded wood. H. 97 cm. Early XVIIIth Century.
From the Convent of Jesus, Aveiro.
Lent by the Museu de Aveiro.

406 Pair of Plinths

Wood, gilt and polychrome. H. 157 cm. Salomonic columns carved with vines and birds, the capitals with cherub-heads and flowers. Early XVIIIth Century.
Lent by the Museu Machado de Castro, Coimbra.

407 Pair of Gilded Doors

Each of eight square panels, superbly carved with flower-heads and emblems tinted with red and surrounded by branching foliage. H. 220 cm.: L. 206 cm. From the celebrated Coro Baixo (Lower Choir) of the Convento de Jesus at Aveiro. Early XVIIIth Century.
Lent by the Convento de Jesus, Aveiro.

408 A Flying Angel

Polychrome wood. H. 62 cm. XVIIth Century. From the Church of Almedina, Coimbra.
Lent by the Museu Machado de Castro, Coimbra.

409 Figures from a Crib (*Presepio*)

Polychrome terracotta. Various dimensions. Late XVIIIth Century.
Lent by the Museu de Arte Antiga, Lisbon.

410 Altar-cloth

Red velvet, embroidered in gold. 99 × 270 cm. With applied enrichments in yellow. XVIIth Century.
Lent by the Museu Machado de Castro, Coimbra.

411 Covered Jar

Silver. H. 39 cm. The shape derived from local Portuguese pottery. Engraved with festoons and leaves. Marked *P* (Porto) and *LAC* (Luis Antonio T. Coelho). 1792–1810.
Lent by the Sé do Porto.

412 Arraiolos Carpet

Wool embroidery. 375 × 180 cm. Design based on Persian motifs, in polychrome. XVIIth Century.
Lent by the Museu Machado de Castro, Coimbra.

413 **Arraiolos Carpet**
Wool embroidery. 350 × 145 cm. Persian design in polychrome.
Late XVIIth Century. From the Monastery of São Bento, Évora.
Lent by the Museu de Arte Antiga, Lisbon.

414 **Arm Chair**
Wood, gilt and lavishly carved in rococo style; the seat and back
covered with figured crimson damask. H. 167 cm. Third quarter of
the XVIIIth Century.
Lent by the Fundação da Casa de Bragança, Vila Viçosa.

Attributed to PIERRE ANTOINE QUILLARD (1711–*c.* 1735)
415 **King John V**
Canvas 100 × 82 cm. Quillard, French painter in the style of
Watteau, settled in Portugal in 1729 and became painter to the Court
and a member of the Lisbon Academy.
Lent by the Fundação Ricardo Espirito Santo, Lisbon.

416 **Bedspread**
Red damask. 275 × 210 cm. XVIIIth Century.
Lent by the Fundação Ricardo Espirito Santo, Lisbon.

417 **Secretaire**
Lignum vitae. Serpentine front; canted corners with carved consoles
headed by masks; brass mounts in rococo style. H. 128 cm.: W. 125
cm. Middle of the XVIIIth Century (period of King John V).
Lent by the Fundação Ricardo Espirito Santo, Lisbon.

418 **Writing-Chair**
Lignum vitae. H. 100 cm. Serpentine seat-rail centring in satyr-
mask; cabriole legs. Carved with scrolls and foliage in rococo style,
the arms inlaid. Third quarter of the XVIIIth Century.
Lent by the Duques de Palmela, Lisbon.

419 **Pair of Candlesticks**
Silver. H. 26 cm. Octagonal fluted stem, the base decorated with
shells and palms. The Arms of Dom Tomaz d'Almeida. Early
XVIIIth Century.
Lent by the Museu de Arte Antiga, Lisbon.

420   Armorial Tankard and Cover

Cut-glass.   H. 20 cm.   Engraved with the Royal Coat of Arms and the monogram C R, of Queen Carlota Joaquina.   Vista Alegre ware. Early XIXth Century.
Lent by the Fundação da Casa de Bragança, Vila Viçosa.

421   Inkstand

Silver, parcel-gilt.   L. 29 cm.   Octagonal base on eight ball-feet, decorated with festoons and leaves.   The Arms of Cardinal Mendonça (1786–1808).   Marked *XI* (Assay) and *João Luis Freire*.   Neo-classic style.
Lent by the Museu de Arte Antiga, Lisbon.

422   Armchair

Wood, gilt, carved with rococo scrolls and foliage.   Cabriole legs, the seat and back covered with red velvet.   H. 161 cm.
Lent by the Museu de Arte Antiga, Lisbon.

423   Pair of Altar Torchères

Gilt wood on paw feet: wreathed bases support a vase and shaft, carved with swags, *paterae* and drooping leaves, the lamp-holders of gilded metal.   H. 215 cm.
Lent by the Convento de Arouca.

424   Chair

Walnut.   The cresting and seat-rail carved with foliage; cabriole legs; the seat and back of leather, with painted and gilt chinoiserie decoration.   H. 113 cm.   *c.* 1760.
Lent by the Museu Soares dos Reis, Oporto.

425   Organ

The case japanned with chinoiserie subjects in polychrome. H. 128 cm.; W. 96 cm.   Middle of the XVIIIth Century.
Lent by the Conservatorio Nacional, Lisbon.

DOMINGOS ANTÓNIO DE SEQUEIRA (1768–1837)

426   Portrait of a Boy

Canvas.   49 × 39 cm.   Painted *c.* 1800.
Lent by Professor Reynaldo dos Santos, Lisbon.

427 Mirror and Pier Table

Wood, carved with neo-classic and other motives in gilt on a grey background; the table marble-topped. H. 309 cm. Late XVIIIth Century.
Lent by the Fundação Ricardo Espirito Santo, Lisbon.

428 Small Frieze of Tiles (Azulejos)

Decorated with flowers and birds in neo-classic style. 90×250 cm. Late XVIIIth Century.
Lent by the Museu de Arte Antiga, Lisbon.

429 Arraiolos Carpet

Wool embroidery. 327 × 197 cm. Flowers and parrots in blue and yellow. Early XVIIIth Century.
Lent by the Palácio Nacional de Queluz.

430 Octagonal Vase

Porcelain. H. 19·5 cm. Decorated with butterflies and roses and marked with the Crown and *V. A.* Vista Alegre ware. Early XIXth Century.
Lent by the Fábrica da Vista Alegre.

431 Bust of Queen Maria I

Faience. H. 90 cm. Lisbon, Rato ware. Late XVIIIth Century.
Lent by the Palácio de Queluz.

432 Vase

Porcelain. H. 25·5 cm. Empire style. Vista Alegre ware. Early XIXth Century.
Lent by the Museu de Arte Antiga, Lisbon.

433 Armchair

Lignum vitae. H. 102 cm. Lyre back and claw feet; carved in rococo style, the seat of green damask. Mid-XVIIIth Century.
Lent by the Museu d'Évora.

FRANCISCO VIEIRA PORTUENSE (1765–1805)

434 Angelica Kauffman painting

Canvas. 87 × 66 cm. (oval). Vieira married a daughter of Bartolozzi and spent several years in Italy, where this portrait was presumably painted.
Lent by the Museu de Arte Antiga, Lisbon.

85

435 Arraiolos Carpet
Wool embroidery. 335 × 172 cm. Polychrome decoration of Persian inspiration. XVIIth Century.
Lent by the Museu Machado de Castro, Coimbra.

436 Round Table
Lemon-wood, decorated with marquetry of rosewood, lignum vitae and other woods. The top covered in red velvet. On four arched feet. H. 69 cm. Signed: *José Aniceto Raposo a fẽs ao Loreto em Lisboa.* Late XVIIIth Century.
Lent by the Fundação Ricardo Espirito Santo, Lisbon.

437 Cup and Saucer
Porcelain. Decorated with landscapes in polychrome by Fabre Lusitano. Vista Alegre ware. Early XIXth Century.
Lent by the Fábrica da Vista Alegre.

438 Cup and Plate
Porcelain. Butterflies and insects in polychrome. Vista Alegre ware; XIXth Century.
Lent by the Fábrica da Vista Alegre.

439 Cup and Saucer
Porcelain. Flowers in polychrome. Vista Alegre ware; XIXth Century.
Lent by the Fábrica da Vista Alegre.

440 Plate
Porcelain. A bunch of flowers in the centre. Vista Alegre ware; XIXth Century.
Lent by the Fábrica da Vista Alegre.

441 Teapot
Porcelain. H. 15 cm. Decorated in blue, green and gold. Vista Alegre ware. Early XIXth Century.
Lent by the Fábrica da Vista Alegre.

442 Chair
Wood, with cane seat and peacock-feathers below the top rail. H. 98 cm. Late XVIIIth Century.
Lent by the Palácio de Queluz.

GALLERY VI

443 Chair
Wood, painted with the Royal Arms. H. 89 cm. Late XVIIIth Century.
Lent by Eng°. H. Chaves, Lisbon.

444 Chair
Wood, carved and painted in gilt and polychrome in neo-classic style. Heart-shaped back, cane seat. H. 90 cm. End of the XVIIIth Century.
Lent by Comandante Ernesto de Vilhena, Lisbon.

445 Armchair
Walnut, with gilt carving, the back surmounted by Royal Arms; the seat upholstered in silk. H. 135 cm. First half of the XVIIIth Century (style of King John V).
Lent by the Museu de Arte Antiga, Lisbon.

446 Bedspread
White silk with coloured silk embroidery. 256 × 190 cm. A crown and two birds in the centre. Indo-Portuguese work, late XVIIth Century.
Lent by the Museu de Arte Antiga, Lisbon.

DOMINGOS ANTÓNIO DE SEQUEIRA (1768–1837)
447 The Conde de Farrobo
Canvas. 102 × 62 cm. Painted c. 1800.
Lent by the Museu de Arte Antiga, Lisbon.

448 Mirror
Gilded wood. Rose-coloured moulding, and neo-classic decoration. H. 83 cm.: W. 50 cm. Late XVIIIth Century (style of Queen Maria I).
Lent by the Fundação Ricardo Espirito Santo, Lisbon.

DOMINGOS ANTÓNIO DE SEQUEIRA (1768–1837)
449 The Painter's Children, Domingos and Mariana
Canvas. 88 × 70 cm. Painted in 1816. Exh: Paris, 1931.
Lent by the Museu de Arte Antiga, Lisbon.

450 Commode

Walnut, veneered and inlaid with satinwood and various woods; marble top. H. 87 cm.: W. 120 cm. End of the XVIIIth Century (style of Queen Maria I).
Lent by the Fundação Ricardo Espirito Santo, Lisbon.

451 Pair of Candlesticks

Silver. H. 33 cm. The shape derived from Chinese pagodas. Inscribed in open-work lettering: *Lisboa Pátria do Principe Regente.* Marked *L* (Lisbon) and *BIR* (Bernardo Joaquim Rodrigues— registered 1809). Made for the Regent John VI (1809–1816).
Lent by Comandante Ernesto de Vilhena, Lisbon.

452 Fluted Goblet

Glass. H. 14·2 cm. Vista Alegre ware. Early XIXth Century.
Lent by the Fábrica da Vista Alegre.

453 Jar and Lid

Cut-glass. H. 51 cm. Vista Alegre ware. Early XIXth Century.
Lent by the Duques de Palmela, Lisbon.

454 Bowl

Moulded glass. H. 17 cm. Vista Alegre ware. Early XIXth Century.
Lent by Exmo· S^r· Armando Couto, Oporto.

455 Armorial Plate

Glass. Diam. 22·3 cm. Engraved with the Arms of Portugal and the inscription: *Viva Ioannes V.* Royal Factory of Coina. Early XVIIIth Century.
Lent by the Museu Soares dos Reis, Oporto.

456 Armchair

Wood, gilt and carved decoration in neo-classic style, the seat and back covered with embroidered scarlet damask. H. 131 cm. Late XVIIIth Century.
Lent by the Palácio de Queluz.

457 Arraiolos Carpet

Wool embroidery. 282 × 145 cm. Portuguese design in blue and yellow. Early XVIIIth Century.
Lent by the Palácio de Queluz.

458 Centre Table

Lignum vitae, carved and turned. Top inlaid with parquetry of various woods. Mounts of brass scroll work. H. 79 cm.: W. 97 cm.: L. 184 cm. Late XVIIth Century.

Lent by the Fundação Ricardo Espirito Santo, Lisbon.

459 Toilet Set of 31 Pieces in its Travelling Case

The case covered in red morocco, lined with green velvet and with chased ormolu hasps. H. 45 cm. The elaborate toilet set of silver-gilt lightly engraved with lappets and marked *L* (Lisbon) and *TC*. *c.* 1700.

Lent by the Fundação Ricardo Espirito Santo, Lisbon.

In the Entrance to Central Hall

460 Lamp

Silver and bronze. Faceted triangular form with Angels holding the three chains framed with stems of leaves. Second quarter of the XVIIIth Century.

Lent by the Museu Machado de Castro, Coimbra.

CENTRAL HALL

462 Arraiolos Carpet

Wool embroidery. 170 × 342 cm. Decorated in blues, greens and yellows, with a design of Persian influence. XVIIth Century.
Lent by the Museu Machado de Castro, Coimbra.

463 Frieze of Tiles (Azulejos) representing Lisbon before the Earthquake of 1755

In blue and white: overall dimensions of the frieze, 105 × 2100 cm. Part of the frieze executed for the Palácio dos Condes de Tentúgal, Lisbon, *c.* 1720–1730.
Lent by the Museu de Arte Antiga, Lisbon.

464 Children's Carriage

Cabriolet type. H. 150 cm.; L. 352 cm.; W. 148 cm. The panels painted with Pompeian themes in polychrome on gilt, the gilded mountings carved in wood in rococo style. Upholstered in red velvet, with a red morocco apron. The leather saddle incised with the Royal Arms and mounted in gilt bronze. Made for the children of Queen Maria I for use in the Royal Parks. Late XVIIIth Century. From the Palácio Real de Quèluz.
Lent by the Museu dos Coches, Lisbon.

465 Arraiolos Carpet

Wool embroidery in blue and yellow. 279·4 × 147·3 cm. Decorated with animals in Portuguese style. XVIIth Century.
Lent by the Victoria and Albert Museum, London.

466 Bedspread

White linen with coloured silk embroidery. 221 × 149 cm. The Tree of Life, and Birds. XVIIIth Century. Castelo Branco style.
Lent by the Museu de Arte Antiga, Lisbon.

467 Pelmet

Gilt wood heavily carved and pierced in rococo style. H. 97 cm.; L. 168 cm. Second half of the XVIIIth Century.
Lent by the Museu de Aveiro.

90

468 Chair

Walnut and embossed leather. H. 135 cm. Second half of the XVIIth Century.
Lent by the Museu de Arte Antiga, Lisbon.

469 Chair

Lignum vitae and embossed leather; the back with the initials *GIS*.
H. 93 cm. Mid-XVIIIth Century.
Lent by the Museu de Arte Antiga, Lisbon.

In Case N (Nos. 470–484)

470 Jug

Faience. H. 27 cm. Decorated with standing musicians. Oporto, Massarelos ware. Late XVIIIth Century.
Lent by Exmo. Sr. Armando Couto, Oporto.

471 Ewer and Basin

Faience. H. 31 cm. (the Ewer); L. 41 cm. (the Basin). Polychrome floral decoration. The ewer helmet-shaped. Late XVIIIth Century.
Lent by the Museu de Arte Antiga, Lisbon.

472 Dish

Faience. Diam. 32 cm. Decorated with a man o' war in the central medallion. Oporto, Rocha Soares ware. XVIIIth Century.
Lent by the Museu de Arte Antiga, Lisbon.

473 Tureen

Faience. H. 23 cm.; Diam. 37 cm. Decorated with landscapes in polychrome. XVIIIth Century.
Lent by the Museu de Arte Antiga, Lisbon.

474 Coffee-pot

Faience. H. 33 cm. With floral decoration in blue and manganese. Oporto, Cavaquinho ware. Marked *FRP.* Early XIXth Century.
Lent by the Museu de Arte Antiga, Lisbon.

475 Cruet

Faience. H. 10 cm. Decorated with landscapes in polychrome. Lisbon, late XVIIIth Century.
Lent by the Museu Soares dos Reis, Oporto.

476 Tureen

Faience. H. 37·5 cm. Decorated with flowers in polychrome; the pierced cover with an artichoke knop. XVIIIth Century, probably Lisbon, Bica do Sapato ware.
Lent by the Museu de Arte Antiga, Lisbon.

477 Ewer and Basin

Faience. H. 27·5 cm. (the Ewer); L. 36·8 cm. (the Basin). Decorated with landscapes in polychrome. Lisbon, Bica do Sapato ware. XVIIIth Century.
Lent by the Museu de Arte Antiga, Lisbon.

478 Covered Jug

Faience. H. 41·5 cm. With neo-classic decoration in polychrome. Coimbra, early XIXth Century.
Lent by the Museu Machado de Castro, Coimbra.

479 Ewer and Basin

Faience. H. 28·5 cm. (the Ewer); Diam. 36·8 cm. (the Basin). Decorated with flowers in polychrome; the ewer helmet-shaped. Oporto, XVIIIth Century.
Lent by the Museu de Arte Antiga, Lisbon.

480 Covered Jug

Faience. H. 31 cm. Decorated with flowers in polychrome. Lisbon, early XIXth Century.
Lent by the Museu de Arte Antiga, Lisbon.

481 Vase

Faience. H. 23 cm. With pierced shoulders and floral decoration in polychrome. Marked *FRTB* (Tomás Bruneto). Lisbon, Rato ware. XVIIIth Century.
Lent by the Museu de Arte Antiga, Lisbon.

482 Vase

Faience. H. 27 cm. Decorated with two female figures and inscribed: *REAL FABRICA DE CUSTODIO FR.ᴬ BRAGA.* XVIIIth Century.
Lent by the Museu de Arte Antiga, Lisbon.

483 Plate

Faience. Diam. 21·8 cm. Decorated with a female figure in contemporary costume. Oporto, Gaia ware. Late XVIIIth Century.
Lent by the Museu Soares dos Reis, Oporto.

484 Armorial Casket

Faience. 31 × 27 cm. Decorated in relief with the Royal Arms of Portugal on the lid. Lisbon, Rato ware. XVIIIth Century.
Lent by the Museu de Arte Antiga, Lisbon.

---

485 Arraiolos Carpet

Wool embroidery in polychrome. 292·1 × 137·2 cm. The design of Persian inspiration. Early XVIIth Century.
Lent by the Victoria and Albert Museum, London.

486 Four-chair Settee

Chestnut. Simple rectangular back and seat panels upholstered in boldly stamped leather; turned legs and stretchers. H. 107 cm.: L. 178 cm. XVIIth Century.
Lent by the Museu de Arte Antiga, Lisbon.

487 Schabraque (Horsecloth)

Olive-green velvet with applied ornamentation and Episcopal Arms. L. 147 cm. XVIIIth Century.
Lent by the Museu Machado de Castro, Coimbra.

JOSEFA DE OBIDOS (1634–1684)

488 The Month of March

Canvas. 113 × 172 cm. Dated *1668*.
Lent by Ex^(mo.) S^(r.) Augusto de Siqueira, Lisbon.

489 Schabraque (Horsecloth)

Blue velvet with applied ornamentation and Episcopal Arms. L. 147 cm. XVIIIth Century.
Lent by the Museu Machado de Castro, Coimbra.

In Case O (Nos. 490–503)

490 **Ewer and Shaving Bowl**

Silver. (Ewer) H. 28·5 cm.; (Bowl) L. 35 cm. Ewer decorated with flowers and leaves; scroll-handle with acanthus. The bowl in the shape of a shell. Marked *G* (Guimarães) and *ME*. Mid-XVIIIth Century.
Lent by the Fundação Ricardo Espirito Santo, Lisbon.

491 **Tea-pot**

Silver. H. 21 cm. Inverted pear-shaped, rococo style. Marked *P* (Porto), *NM* and *ANR* (Lisbon). 1768–1792.
Lent by the Museu de Arte Antiga, Lisbon.

492 **Coffee-pot**

Silver. H. 28 cm. Tapering cylindrical shape with rococo decoration. Middle of the XVIIIth Century.
Lent by the Fundação Ricardo Espirito Santo, Lisbon.

493 **Altar Vessels and Tray**

Silver-gilt. (Vessels) H. 15 cm.; (Tray) L. 28 cm. Pear-shape, twisted fluting and rococo decoration. The tray with gadrooned rim. Mid-XVIIIth Century (the tray perhaps earlier).
Lent by the Museu de Lamego.

494 **Ewer and Dish**

Silver. (Bowl) L. 55·5 cm. The ewer, helmet-shaped and decorated with masks in rococo style. Marked *P* (Porto) and *IF* (1758–1768).
Lent by Exma. S^{ra.} Dona Amélia de Freitas G. Carvalho, Lisbon.

495 **Coffee-pot**

Silver. H. 26 cm. Decorated with undulating fluting and garlands of roses. Marked *P* (Porto) and *LAC* (Luis Antonio T. Coelho). May be dated from the mark 1768–1792.
Lent by Exmo. Sr. Antonio Pedro da Silva, Lisbon.

496 **Coffee-pot**

Silver. H. 25 cm. Oval shape, undecorated except for lightly engraved bands of roses and leaves. Marked *XI* (Assay) and *MIM*. Mid-XVIIIth Century.
Lent by Exmo. Sr. Pedro da Silva, Lisbon.

497   **Hour-glass**

Silver. H. 30 cm. Six claw feet and three balusters embossed with flowers. The Royal Arms of Portugal. Inscribed: *Da Meza da Consiencia e Ordens.* Mid-XVIIIth Century.

Lent by the Museu de Arte Antiga, Lisbon.

498   **Altar Vessels**

Silver-gilt. H. 19 cm. Double-baluster shape, with the Arms of Bishop Julio Francisco d'Oliveira (1740–1755).

Lent by the Museu de Sé de Viseu.

499   **Coffee-pot on three Feet**

Silver. H. 30 cm. Engraved with ribbon-ties. Marked *L* (Lisbon) and *DF* (*c.* 1750–1770).

Lent by the Fundação Ricardo Espirito Santo, Lisbon.

500   **Jug**

Silver. H. 26 cm. Flattened oval shape with rococo decoration; base encircled with laurel. Marked *P* (Porto) and *AIV* (1758–1768).

Lent by Dr. Guilherme Moreira, Lisbon.

501   **Coffee-pot**

Silver. H. 25 cm. Flattened oval shape, rococo style. Marked *P* (Porto) and *LAC* (Luis Antonio Coelho). May be dated from the mark 1768–1792.

Lent by the Fundação Ricardo Espirito Santo, Lisbon.

502   **Ewer and Shaving Bowl**

Silver. (Ewer) H. 27·8 cm.; (Bowl) L. 28·5 cm. The ewer embossed with waves, the bowl in the shape of a shell. Marked *P* (Porto) and *AD* (1768–1792).

Lent by Dr. Guilherme Moreira, Lisbon.

503   **Tea-pot**

Silver. H. 17·8 cm. Pear-shaped, rococo chasing. Marked with the head of an old man. Mid-XVIIIth Century.

Lent by Dr. Guilherme Moreira, Lisbon.

In Case P (Nos. 504–519).

504   **Ewer**

Silver. H. 27·5 cm. Baluster-shaped, with rococo decoration. Style of John V.

Lent by the Museu de S. Roque, Lisbon.

505　Shell-shaped Dish

Silver.　L. 38 cm.　At the back engraved with wave-motive, and on three snail feet.　c. 1700.
Lent by the Museu de S. Roque, Lisbon.

506　Two Plates

Silver.　Diam. 24·5 cm.　Plain, with the Arms of Moura, Salvador and Aguiares.　Marked *L* (Lisbon) and *IL* (1720–1740).
Lent by the Fundação Ricardo Espirito Santo, Lisbon.

507　Salver on Four Feet

Silver.　Diam. 23·5 cm.　Shell-shaped feet, scalloped border decorated with scrolls.　Marked *L* (Lisbon) and *JCL* (1720—*c.* 1750).
Lent by the Fundação Ricardo Espirito Santo, Lisbon.

508　Two Knives

Silver.　L. 26·5 cm.　With scimitar blades.　Period of John V (1706–1750).
Lent by the Fundação Ricardo Espirito Santo, Lisbon.

509　Salver on Foot

Silver-gilt.　H. 17 cm.; Diam. 30 cm.　Strap-work chasing, with the Arms of Bishop Julio Francisco d'Oliveira (1740–1755).
Lent by the Museu Grão Vasco, Viseu.

510　Coffee-pot

Silver.　H. 21 cm.　Flattened oval shape with bands of light engraving.　Marked *B* (Braga) and *APR*..　Style of John V (1720–*c.* 1750).
Lent by Dr. José d'Alpuim, Viana do Castelo.

511　Holy Water Stoup and Sprinkler

Silver-gilt.　H. 17 cm.　Decorated with rosettes.　The stoup and handle decorated with satyr masks.　Early XVIIIth Century. Style of John V.
Lent by the Duques de Palmela, Lisbon.

512　Ewer and Dish

Silver.　(Ewer) H. 31 cm.; (Bowl) L. 54 cm.　Gadrooned and decorated with scrolls and geometrical designs.　A Coat of Arms in the centre of the dish.　Marked *L* (Lisbon) and *FMR* (1720–*c.* 1750).
Lent by the Fundação Ricardo Espirito Santo, Lisbon.

513 Ewer and Dish

Silver-gilt. (Ewer) H. 23 cm.; (Dish) L. 18·5 cm. The ewer in the shape of a tea-pot. Heavily chased with strapwork. The Arms of the Sousas de Arronches. Second quarter of the XVIIIth Century.
Lent by the Museu Soares dos Reis, Oporto.

514 Coffee-pot

Silver. H. 27 cm. Oval form, fluted. With the Arms of Bishop Julio Francisco d'Oliveira (1740–1755). Style of John V.
Lent by the Museu Grão Vasco, Viseu.

515 Salver on Foot

Silver-gilt. H. 17 cm.; Diam. 34 cm. Chased decoration with the Arms of Sousas de Arronches. Second quarter of the XVIIIth Century.
Lent by the Museu Soares dos Reis, Oporto.

516 Perfume Burner

Silver. Diam. 13 cm. Shaped base. Embossed with shells and a mask; a wooden scroll handle. Marked *L* (Lisbon) and *OJR* (?) (*c.* 1720–1750). Arms of Sousa, Silva, Freire and Alte. Style of John V.
Lent by the Marqueses de Sá da Bandeira, Lisbon.

517 Candle-holder

Silver. L. 38 cm. Heavily chased. Second quarter of the XVIIIth Century. Style of John V.
Lent by the Museu Soares dos Reis, Oporto.

518 Canteen of Silver for twelve

Tortoise-shell, velvet-lined. H. 42 cm. Marked *L* (Lisbon) and *LA* (1720–*c.* 1750). Style of John V.
Lent by the Fundação Ricardo Espirito Santo, Lisbon.

519 Ewer

Silver. H. 27·5 cm. Chased decoration and with a large leaf gathered under the spout. Marked *L* (Lisbon) and *MF* (1720–*c.* 1750). Style of John V.
Lent by the Museu de S. Roque, Lisbon.

520   Schabraque (Horsecloth)

Green velvet with applied ornaments of solid silver.   With the Arms
of the Cadaval family.   L. 170 cm.   Late XVIIIth Century.
Lent by the Fundação Ricardo Espirito Santo, Lisbon.

521   Salomonic Column

Wood.   H. 168 cm.   Gilded and carved with a cherub, vines and
birds.   Early XVIIIth Century.
Lent by the Museu Machado de Castro, Coimbra.

522   Pair of Fluted Columns

Gilt Wood.   H. 216 cm.   The capitals carved with acanthus, the
bases with winged cherub-heads and foliage.   Renaissance style,
early XVIIth Century.
Lent by the Museu Machado de Castro, Coimbra.

523   Arraiolos Carpet

Wool embroidery.   112 × 169 cm.   Portuguese design with parrots
and animals in blues and yellows.   Early XVIIIth Century.   From
the Convent of Santa Clara, Vila do Conde.
Lent by the Museu de Arte Antiga, Lisbon.

524   Part of an Altar

Gilded wood.   H. 144 cm.   Deeply carved with pelicans and foliage.
Late XVIIth or early XVIIIth Century.
Lent by the Museu Machado de Castro, Coimbra.

525   Jar

Faience.   H. 27 cm.   Chinoiserie panels in blue and manganese.
XVIIth Century.
Lent by the Museu Machado de Castro, Coimbra.

526   Children's Carriage

Cabriolet type.   H. 140 cm.; L. 339 cm.; W. 140 cm.   Almost
identical with No. 464 in style and decoration, but of smaller
dimensions.
Lent by the Museu dos Coches, Lisbon.

527 The State Coach of Queen Maria Francisca

The body, to seat four, of carved and gilded wood, painted with flowers and cupids in polychrome on a gilt ground on surrounding panels, with the Arms of the Queen between emblematic supporters on the front and back panels and on the doors. The roof of shaped leather with four urn finials. Upholstered in red velvet. The chassis and wheels gilded and carved with masks and rococo motifs in relief. L. 600 cm.; H. 290 cm.; W. 160 cm. Made for Queen Maria Francisca of Savoy, the Consort of King Afonso VI, in about 1670. *Lent by the Museu dos Coches, Lisbon.*

LARGE SOUTH ROOM

529 Side-table

Teak and lignum vitae, with inlay of foliage and mythical birds picked out in ivory. Three drawers with cut brass mounts. H. 83 cm.; L. 124 cm.; W. 75 cm. Indo-Portuguese work, XVIIth Century.
Lent by the Museu de Arte Antiga, Lisbon.

530 Indo-Persian Carpet (with Portuguese Caravels)

Polychrome wools. 310 × 700 cm. Persian design with Portuguese figures and ships. Early XVIIth Century.
Lent by Lord Sackville.

531 Cabinet on Stand

Ebony and oriental woods. Inlays of ivory and oriental wood. Cut brass mounts. The stand with corner supports of mermaids. H. 126 cm.; W. 90 cm. Indo-Portuguese work, XVIIth Century.
Lent by the Fundação Ricardo Espirito Santo, Lisbon.

532 Mass or Credence Table

Indian woods, decorated with Indian figures, elephants, mythical birds and fish, inlaid in bone; in the central medallion a Portuguese Monstrance, surrounded by angels and the inscription: *LOVVADO SEIA OSANTISSIMO SACRAMENTO.* H. 106·7 cm.; W. 83·8 cm. Exh: R.A. 1947–8 (1338). Indo-Portuguese work, early XVIIth Century. From the Jesuit Chapel at Lahore.
Lent by the Victoria and Albert Museum, London.

UNKNOWN INDO-PORTUGUESE ARTIST (Mid-XVIth Century)
533 Afonso de Albuquerque

Panel 182 × 105 cm. Posthumous portrait (much restored) by the same hand as No. 539. Afonso de Albuquerque, perhaps the greatest Viceroy of Portuguese India.
Lent by the Governador Geral da Índia Portuguesa.

534 Cabinet on Stand

Oriental woods, decorated with mythical birds and foliage in wood and bone inlay. Eighteen drawers with cut brass mounts. H. 131 cm.; W. 91 cm. Indo-Portuguese work, XVIIth Century.
Lent by the Victoria and Albert Museum, London.

535 Ewer shaped as an Exotic Bird

Silver. H. 53 cm. The bird has another small bird in its mouth: its wings and back are decorated in fish-scale ornament. Oriental style, probably Indo-Portuguese work. XVIIth Century.
Lent by Exmo. Sr. Pedro Costa, Lisbon.

536 Bedspread

Cotton embroidered with red and gold silk. 320×249 cm. The border decorated with scenes of Portuguese hunting in India. In the centre, Portuguese Arms and ships and double-headed eagles. Indo-Portuguese work, XVIIth Century.
Lent by the Victoria and Albert Museum, London.

537 Chest

Ebony and teak, with inlay picked out in ivory. Metalwork of cut brass. On four gilt lion feet. H. 76 cm.; L. 127 cm.; W. 88 cm. Indo-Portuguese work, XVIIth Century.
Lent by the Museu de Arte Antiga, Lisbon.

538 Reliquary

Silver, with gold and blue velvet. A gold Christ on a relic-filled cross is flanked by the Virgin, St. John and other Saints in silver with polychrome tinting on a silver filigree background; above, an oval miniature of the Virgin and Child beneath a scroll and finial; the circular silver base embossed with animals and vines. H. 66 cm. Indo-Portuguese work. XVIIth Century. From the Convent of Carmo da Vidigueira.
Lent by the Museu de Arte Antiga, Lisbon.

UNKNOWN INDO-PORTUGUESE ARTIST (Mid-XVIth Century)

539 Dom John de Castro

Panel. 186 × 97 cm. Dom John de Castro (1500–1548), Viceroy of Portuguese India, died in Goa, where this portrait was painted. (Much restored.)
Lent by the Governador Geral da Índia Portuguesa.

540 Cabinet on Stand

Teak, lignum vitae and ebony. H. 143 cm.: L. 104 cm.: W. 54 cm.
Inlaid, the upper lid blazoned with the Arms of the Realm, sur-
mounted by a coronet of floral ornaments, possibly the badge of
Lancaster or Braganza. Metalwork of cut brass. Indo-Portu-
guese work, XVIIth Century.
Lent by the Museu de Arte Antiga, Lisbon.

541 Ewer in the form of an Exotic Bird

Silver. H. 48·5 cm. The head heavily chased, the body and wings
chased with large scales. Oriental style, possibly Indo-Portuguese,
later adapted as a perfume burner in Braga. Marked on the cover of
the perfume burner *B* (Braga) and *IG* (?). XVIIth Century.
Lent by Exmo. S^r. Pedro Silva, Lisbon.

542 Indo-Persian Carpet (with Portuguese Caravels)

Polychrome wools. 386 × 666 cm. Persian design with Portuguese
figures and ships. Early XVIIth Century.
Lent by the Musée Historique des Tissues, Lyon.

543 Pair of Japanese Screens

Each screen 171 × 380 cm., in six leaves. Japanese painting on a gilt
ground depicting the arrival of a Portuguese ship in Japan, *c.* 1600.
Lent by the Ministério das Finanças.

544 Bedspread

Embroidered silk on cotton. 320 × 268 cm. Biblical and historical
scenes in blue on cream, with the Arms of a Portuguese bishop in the
centre. The inscriptions in Portuguese. Indo-Portuguese work,
XVIIth Century.
Lent by Senhor Ferreira Pinto, Lisbon.

545 Bedspread

White cotton embroidered with red and yellow silk. 288 × 202 cm.
A pelican in the centre; hunting scenes with figures in Portuguese
dress. Indo-Portuguese work, early XVIIth Century.
Lent by the Museu de Arte Antiga, Lisbon.

546 Flemish Tapestry with Indo-Portuguese Subjects

Wool and silk. 290 × 368 cm. Representing Portuguese and Indian
figures, with giraffes and elephants.
Lent by the Fundação Ricardo Espirito Santo, Lisbon.

547 Bedspread

Linen, embroidered in yellow and red silk. 290 × 220 cm. Indo-Portuguese work. Late XVIth Century.
Lent by the Museu Machado de Castro, Coimbra.

548 Lid of a Chinese Chest

Wood, gold on red lacquer. 72 × 142 cm. Depicting the arrival of a European mission to China. XVIIIth Century. This is the type of lacquer adapted by the Portuguese craftsmen of Coimbra in the time of King John V.
Lent by Dr. Pedro Batalha Reis, Lisbon.

549 Bedspread

White cotton embroidered with yellow silk. 330 × 280 cm. Depicting Portuguese ships and hunting scenes; figures in Portuguese dress. Indo-Portuguese work, early XVIIth Century.
Lent by the Museu de Arte Antiga, Lisbon.

550 Indo-Persian Carpet (with Portuguese Caravels)

Polychrome wools. 195 × 477 cm. Persian design with Portuguese figures and ships. Early XVIIth Century.
Lent by the Trustees of the C. S. Gulbenkian Foundation.

551 Table

Top in oriental wood with ebony inlay. The quadrangular legs deeply carved with Oriental *motifs*. Four drawers with escutcheons of cut brass. H. 84 cm.; W. 103 cm.; L. 161 cm. Indo-Portuguese work, XVIIth Century.
Lent by the Fundação Ricardo Espirito Santo, Lisbon.

552 Altar Frontal

White damask, embroidered with chinoiserie designs in coloured silks and silver thread, the border and fringe in gold thread. 285 × 105 cm. This type of design is closely akin to the designs of Jean Pillement, who worked in Portugal for many years. XVIIIth Century.
Lent by the Museu Machado de Castro, Coimbra.

553 Chinese Dish

Porcelain. Diam. 20 cm. Probably 1578–1580 (Wan-li). Decorated with the Arms of Matias de Albuquerque, Governor of Malacca in 1577 and Viceroy of Portuguese India in 1591.
Lent by the Museu de Arte Antiga, Lisbon.

554 Chinese Wine Bottle

Porcelain. H. 26 cm. Of the Chêng-tê period (1506–1521), but, as often, with the false mark of an earlier dynasty (Hsüan-tê). Decorated with the Manueline emblem, the Armillary Sphere. It may be dated with certainty between 1516, the year of the arrival in China of the Portuguese envoy Tomé Pires, and the death of King Manuel in 1521. A most important documentary piece and the earliest identified Chinese porcelain commissioned for the European market.
Lent by a Private Collector, Lisbon.

555 Chinese Two-handled Cup

Porcelain. H. 18 cm.; Diam. 16 cm. Dated *1541*. Decorated with a galloping horse outside, in blue, and inside a Buddhist figure. Inscribed inside the rim: *EM TEMPO DE PERO DE FARIA DE 541*. Of the Chia-ching period (1522–1566), but, as often, with the false mark of an earlier dynasty (Hsüan-tê). Portuguese commissions in China are known from at least as early as 1521 (*cf.* No. 554), but this is the earliest Ming piece bearing a date and a European inscription. Pero de Faria was Governor of Malacca from 1537–1543.
Lent by the Junta do Baixo Alentejo, Béja.

556 Chinese Porcelain Bottle

Porcelain. H. 26 cm. Decorated with birds, flowers, the lotus and Buddhist emblems in blue. False mark of *Ta Ming nien Tsao* and inscribed: *ISTO MANDOV EASER JORGE ANRZ IN ERA DE 1557 REINA. . . .* Made in China for a Portuguese client in 1557.
Lent by the Victoria and Albert Museum, London.

557 Japanese Boxes

Gold and silver lacquer on black ground, with Portuguese figures. 27 × 24 × 22 cm. Late XVIth Century.
Lent by the Museu de Arte Antiga, Lisbon.

558 Writing Casket

Carved ivory over gilded wood. H. 18·5 cm.; W. 19·5 cm.; L. 23·8 cm. On the top an Indian scene: on the sides figures in Portuguese costume and friezes of horses. Indo-Portuguese work, early XVIIIth Century.
Lent by the Museu de Arte Antiga, Lisbon.

559 Cingalese Comb

Ivory, set with rubies. L. 17 cm. Carved with elephants, leopards
and other beasts. One of a set of three Cingalese combs probably
bought by Duke Albrecht V of Bavaria with No. 565 in 1566.
Lent by the Bayerische Schlösserverwaltung, Munich.

560 African Ivory Box

H. 19 cm. The top carved as a mounted Portuguese commander,
the base supported by Portuguese soldiers and officials. From Benin
in West Africa. XVIth Century.
Lent by the Museu de Arte Antiga, Lisbon.

561 African Ivory Pyx

Carved with scenes from the Life of the Virgin, the Arms of Portugal
and the Cross of Christ upheld by Angels. The surmounting figure
of the Virgin missing. With the inscription: *AVE GRASIA P.*
H. 14·5 cm. From Portuguese Africa, probably the gift of the King
of the Congo to King John II or King Manuel I. Late XVth Century.
Lent by the Museu Grão Vasco, Viseu.

562 Casket

Pierced silver on wood. H. 16·5 cm.; L. 21·5 cm. Decorated in
European style with flowers and trellis-work; a pineapple finial.
Indo-Portuguese work. XVIIIth Century.
Lent by the Condes de Alcáçovas, Lisbon.

563 Knife-box

Japanese porcelain. H. 30 cm. Decorated in Imari style with
flowers and a Portuguese Coat of Arms. XVIIIth Century.
Lent by the Fundação Ricardo Espirito Santo, Lisbon.

564 Small Chest

Gold filigree, Salamander clasp. H. 10·5 cm.; L. 19·3 cm. Indo-
Portuguese work of the XVIth Century. Given by the widow of the
Viceroy of Portuguese India, Matias d'Albuquerque, to the Monastery
of Graça, Lisbon.
Lent by the Museu de Arte Antiga, Lisbon.

565 Cingalese Jewel Box

Ivory, mounted in gold and set with rubies and sapphires. H.
17·7 cm.; L. 30·5 cm. Carved with scenes commemorating the
diplomatic mission from Ceylon to Portugal in 1542 and the symbolic
crowning of the effigy of the infant Prince Dharmapala by King
John III. Bought in Lisbon by Duke Albrecht V of Bavaria in 1566
for the Treasury of the Residenz, Munich.
Lent by the Bayerische Schlösserverwaltung, Munich.

Manuscripts

566 Chronicle of King Afonso Henriques

Manuscript of 170 leaves, written by Duarte Galvão, *c.* 1520—1530.
The exhibited leaf is the title-page, with a view of Lisbon designed by
Antonio de Olanda.
Lent by the Museu-Biblioteca Conde de Castro Guimarães, Cascais.

567 Genealogy of the Kings of Portugal

Thirteen leaves, commissioned for the Infante Dom Fernando,
brother of King John III, and illuminated by Simon Bening and other
Flemish artists. The exhibited miniature shows a view of Lisbon
designed by Antonio de Olanda. Exh: R.A. 1953 (626).
Lent by the British Museum, London.

568 The Chronicle of (the Conquest of) Guinea

Manuscript on vellum of 161 leaves with illuminated initials. By
Gomez Eanes Dazurara, Commander of the Order of Christ; written
by Joham Gonçalves and finished in February, 1453. On *verso* of l. 5,
a full page miniature, the portrait of Henry the Navigator within a
border of acorns and oak-leaf scrolls, with the motto *Talan de biĕ
faire*: on the opposite page, a similar border with the arms of Henry
the Navigator and the Cross of the Order of Christ, of which he was
Master. The miniature was the key to the identification of all other
portraits of Henry the Navigator: (*cf.* No. 42). Bound in XVIIIth
Century tree-calf with gold-tooled border and red morocco spine.
Size of leaves 32·5 × 23 cm. Coll: Dom Francisco de Joly; Don Juan
Lucas Cortes, 1702.
Lent by the Bibliothèque Nationale, Paris.

569 Leitura Nova

Four volumes from the collection of more than 80 manuscript copies of early Portuguese archives, commissioned by King Manuel I (1495–1521) and continued by King John III (1522–1550). Illuminated by Portuguese artists. The volumes are: (*a*) 4th Book of the Province of Estremadura; (*b*) 4th Book of the Province of Além-Douro; (*c*) 10th Book of the Province of Estremadura; (*d*) 2nd Book of documents of mixed origin. These all date from the first quarter of the XVIth Century. In each case the exhibited page is the title-page.
Lent by the Arquivo Nacional, Lisbon.

570 Coronation Book of the Kings of England

Illuminated Manuscript made in the middle of the XVth Century for use at the Coronation of King Afonso V.
Lent by the Biblioteca Pública de Évora.

571 Illuminated Map by the Cartographer Vaz Dourado

Vellum, 42 folios each 39·4 × 52·1 cm. Inscribed: *ESTE LIVRO FES FERNAÓ VAZ DOVRADO.* Probably made about 1573, as a table of festivals on folio 38 corresponds exactly with that year.
Lent by the British Museum, London.

In the Vestibule

572 Two Angels (Candle-holders)

Polychrome wood. H. 200 cm. Late XVIIth Century. From the Transept of the New Cathedral, Coimbra.
Lent by the Chapter of the Sé Nova, Coimbra.

A SHORT BIBLIOGRAPHY

Arte Portuguesa (3 Vols.), Lisbon, 1955.

BERTAUX, ÉMILE, *La Renaissance en Espagne et en Portugal*, Histoire de l'Art, Vol. IV Paris, 1911.

COUTO, JOÃO, *Pinturas quinhentistas do Sardoal*, Lisbon, 1939.

DE FIGUEIREDO, JOSÉ, *O Pintor Nuno Gonçalves*, Lisbon, 1910.

DE LACERDA, AARÃO, CHICÓ, M. and DOS SANTOS, REYNALDO, *História da Arte em Portugal*, Lisbon, 1942–1955.

DE PAMPLONA, FERNANDO, *Dicionário de Pintores e Escultores Portugueses*, Lisbon, 1954.

DOS SANTOS, REYNALDO, *As Tapeçarias de Arzila e Tânger*, Lisbon, 1920.
———, *Os Primitivos Portugueses*, Lisbon, 1940.
———, *L'Art Portugais*, Paris, 1949 and 1953.
———, *A Escultura em Portugal* (2 Vols.), Lisbon, 1950–52.
———, *Arte Indo-Portuguesa*, Lisbon, 1954.
———, *Nuno Gonçalves*, London, 1955.

DOS SANTOS, REYNALDO, and QUILHÓ, IRENE, *Os Primeiros punções Portugueses Belas Artes* (2nd series), 1953.

FIERENS, PAUL, *Les Primitifs Portugais*, Brussels, 1949.

HUYGHE, RENÉ, *Nuno Gonçalves dans la peinture du XVeme siècle* (*Congrès International de l'Histoire de l'Art*), Lisbon, 1951.

KEIL, LUIS, *As Tapeçarias de D. João de Castro*, Lisbon, 1928.

ROBINSON, J. C., *The Early Portuguese School of Painting*, London, 1866.

SANTOS, LUIS REIS, *Estudos de Pintura Antiga*, Lisbon, 1943.
———, *Vasco Fernandes*, Lisbon, 1946.
———, *Enciclopédia Portuguesa e Brasileira*, Lisbon, 1950.

VAN PUYVELDE, LÉON, *Les Primitifs Portugais et la Peinture Flamande*, Lisbon, 1949.

WATSON, WALTER C., *Portuguese Architecture*, London, 1908.

INDEX OF EXHIBITS

PAINTINGS AND DRAWINGS

SCULPTURE

SCULPTURE (continued)

FAIENCE

FURNITURE

INDEX OF EXHIBITS

INDEX OF LENDERS

113

INDEX OF LENDERS

NOTES

NOTES

NOTES

NOTES

NOTES

NOTES

NOTES

NOTES

NOTES

NOTES

NOTES

NOTES

NOTES

London
WM. CLOWES & SONS, Ltd.
Printers to the Royal Academy